www.BottomLineSecrets.com

Third Printing

Printed in the United States of America

YB06/js

CONTENTS

1 

THE ULTIMATE SOLUTIONS TO HEART DISEASE, STROKE & ALZHEIMER'S

BEYOND CHOLESTEROL: SIX THREATS TO YOUR HEART DOCTORS OFTEN OVERLOOK

Source: **Michael Mogadam, MD,** clinical associate professor of medicine at George Washington University School of Medicine in Washington, DC, and an internist and cholesterol specialist in private practice in Alexandria, VA. He is the author of *Every Heart Attack Is Preventable* (New American Library).

Most doctors believe that elevated cholesterol is the primary cause of heart disease. But seven out of 10 heart attack victims have cholesterol levels in the "borderline" range of 180 to 240.

Clearly, cholesterol levels are important. High levels of LDL (bad) cholesterol or triglycerides and/or lower levels of HDL (good) cholesterol are risk factors. So are smoking, obesity, hypertension and diabetes. **BUT OTHER RISK FACTORS ARE ALSO IMPORTANT...**

CHLAMYDIA INFECTION...

A common respiratory tract germ, *Chlamydia pneumoniae,* can migrate to the arteries and spark an infection that can damage the linings. C. pneumoniae is related to, but different from, the microorganism that causes the sexually transmitted disease commonly known as chlamydia.

More than half of adults with atherosclerosis (hardening of the arteries) are believed to be infected with C. pneumoniae. Only 5% of people with healthy arteries are infected.

SELF-DEFENSE: Anyone with chronic sinusitis or bronchitis who has two or more risk factors for heart disease should have a blood test for C. pneumoniae.

Treatment typically includes a 14-day course of the oral antibiotic *arithromycin* (Zithromax), followed by one pill a week for three months.

DEPRESSED MOOD...

Ten percent of American adults have a syndrome known as HAD—hostility, anger and depression. HAD increases the risk for coronary artery disease as much as high cholesterol or hypertension.

SELF-DEFENSE: People who get frustrated easily...lose their temper...and often display anger should discuss these feelings with their physicians.

Stress-reduction techniques, including meditation, deep breathing and yoga, are helpful. In fact, a recent study at Duke University found that stress reduction can lower the risk for coronary artery disease by 70%.

ELEVATED FIBRINOGEN...

Fibrinogen is a blood protein involved in clotting. An elevated level, above 250 milligrams per deciliter (mg/dl), *triples* the risk for coronary artery disease.

SELF-DEFENSE: People who eat a high-fat diet and have one or more risk factors for heart disease should receive a blood test to measure their fibrinogen levels.

Eliminate fried foods, margarine and other foods that contain trans-fatty acids from your diet. These fats stimulate the liver to produce excess fibrinogen.

ALSO HELPFUL: Eating fatty fish, such as tuna, mackerel and salmon, three or four times per week. The omega-3 fatty acids in fish lower fibrinogen and reduce the risk for blood clots. Taking an 81-milligram (mg) aspirin tablet along with 400 to 800 international units (IU) of vitamin E* daily should also counteract elevated fibrinogen levels.

IMPORTANT: If you have elevated fibrinogen and have suffered a heart attack or stroke or have peripheral-artery disease (poor blood circulation in the legs), your doctor may recommend niacin and/or a cholesterol-lowering drug, such as *pravastatin* (Pravachol).

HIGH HEMATOCRIT...

Hematocrit is the percentage of your whole blood volume that is comprised of red blood cells. At the higher levels—48% to 51%—red blood cells make blood thicker and impair circulation. Elevated hematocrit can *triple* the risk for heart attack.

SELF-DEFENSE: Anyone with a ruddy complexion...morning fatigue...or occasional dizziness or confusion should be tested. Your hematocrit level is routinely measured during blood tests.

Your doctor will need to rule out conditions that increase levels of red blood cells, such as lung or bone marrow disorders.

IF YOU'RE OTHERWISE HEALTHY: Donate one pint of blood every few weeks until your hematocrit level drops to 42% to 45%. Continue donating blood every 90 days to maintain a healthful level.

ELEVATED HOMOCYSTEINE...

An abnormally high level of this blood protein can actually *double* the risk for heart attack and stroke.

An elevated homocysteine level damages artery linings and increases the risk for clots.

SELF-DEFENSE: Anyone with a personal or family history of cardiovascular disease—or with one or more risk factors—should be tested for elevated homocysteine.

If your blood contains more than nine micromoles per liter, ask your doctor about taking B vitamin supplements. I recommend 1,000 to 2,000 micrograms (mcg) each of folate and vitamin B-12 twice daily.

If your homocysteine level remains high after eight to 10 weeks, I recommend supplementing your diet with 50 to 100 mg of vitamin B-6 twice a day.

*Due to the possible interactions between vitamin E and various drugs and supplements as well as other safety considerations, be sure to talk to your doctor before taking vitamin E.

PLATELET ABNORMALITIES...

In some people, blood platelets—cell-like structures that assist in clotting—function more than they should, increasing the risk for clots that can cause heart attack. Excessive platelet levels—above 250,000 per milliliter (ml) of blood—are also a threat.

SELF-DEFENSE: People with one or more heart disease risk factors should receive a blood test to measure platelet levels.

If platelet levels are elevated, take one 81-mg aspirin tablet daily and one 325-mg aspirin every two weeks to boost the effectiveness of your daily low-dose aspirin.

The prescription drug *clopidogrel* (Plavix) also has antiplatelet effects. It is useful for people who are allergic to aspirin.

All men over age 35 and women over 45 should ask their doctors about taking a low-dose aspirin daily—even if they have no coronary risk factors. It may save their hearts—and their lives. ■

THE ULTIMATE CHOLESTEROL-LOWERING DIET

Source: **John McDougall, MD,** founder and medical director of the McDougall Program, a diet and exercise program in Santa Rosa, CA, *www.drmcdougall.com.* He is the author of numerous books, including *The McDougall Program for a Healthy Heart: A Lifesaving Approach to Preventing and Treating Heart Disease* (Plume).

The importance of lowering cholesterol levels was underscored when the National Institutes of Health (NIH) released guidelines calling for aggressive treatment for total cholesterol levels of 240 or higher.

NIH recommended aiming for a level of 200 or below.

With my patients, I go even further—I work with them to achieve and maintain a total cholesterol level *no higher than 150.* This is the point where heart disease stops progressing and begins to reverse itself. This is also a level of cholesterol where the risk of dying from heart disease is almost zero. If you settle for a total cholesterol of 200 instead, you still subject your arteries to toxins and plaque buildup—and risk a heart attack.

Here is how I helped my high-cholesterol patients get their levels under control...

CUT OUT ANIMAL PRODUCTS...

The single most effective way to lower your blood cholesterol is to stop eating foods that contain cholesterol. In other words, *avoid all animal products*—red meat, poultry, shellfish, fish, eggs, dairy products and foods made with them.

As far as the health of your arteries is concerned, there is no "safe" amount in regard to the consumption of animal products.

Forbidden foods (many of which have long been perceived as permissible) include...

- ***Fish and fowl.*** Some studies have shown that these foods will raise cholesterol just as surely as beef or pork.
- ***Low-fat or skim milk,*** cheese or other dairy products. Even when the fat is taken out, the animal proteins in these foods can raise cholesterol levels and damage the artery walls.
- ***"Free" fats such as margarine,*** corn oil, olive oil and canola oil. These fats are easily oxidized in the bloodstream, making plaque likely to build up on artery walls.

If you follow a strict vegetarian diet for several months, you can lower your cholesterol levels by 25% or more. At the same time, blood levels of triglycerides, homocysteine, uric acid and other heart disease risk factors will also decline.

VEGETARIAN DELIGHTS...

Giving up animal products does not mean you must eat poorly. The foods in my program are varied and delicious. They provide all needed nutrients in optimal amounts.

You can eat all you want of the following...

- ***Whole grains,*** including barley, brown rice, buckwheat, bulgur, corn, oatmeal and wheat, as well as noodles that are made from these sources.
- ***Potatoes,*** sweet potatoes and yams.
- ***Root vegetables,*** including beets, carrots and turnips.
- ***Squashes,*** such as acorn, butternut and zucchini squash.
- ***Beans and peas,*** including chickpeas, green peas, kidney beans, lentils and string beans.
- ***Other vegetables,*** such as broccoli, brussels sprouts, cabbage, celery, the darker lettuces, spinach, cucumbers, okra, onions, peppers and mushrooms.
- ***Mild spices*** and cooking herbs.

Eat only limited amounts of fruit and fruit juice (no more than three servings a day), sugar and other sweeteners, salt and fatty plant foods—such as peanut butter, seed spreads, avocados, olives and soybean products, including tofu. Simple sugars, even fruit and juice, raise cholesterol and triglycerides.

HEART-HEALTHFUL MENU PLAN...

There are many excellent vegetarian cookbooks to choose from, but you don't have to be a gourmet to prepare heart-healthful meals. Start with potatoes, rice, beans or spaghetti, then add some low-fat, plant-based sauces and soups. Throw in a salad and bread, and you've got a meal. **OTHER TIPS...**

- ***For breakfast,*** toast, bagels, oatmeal, cereals, hash browns and pancakes (all made from the right ingredients) are all fine. Use rice milk or soy milk on cold cereal.
- ***Sauté food in soy sauce,*** wine or sherry, vinegar (rice or balsamic), vegetarian Worcestershire sauce, salsa, or lemon or lime juice.
- ***Eat until you're satisfied...***and eat as often as you need to.
- ***To boost feelings of fullness,*** include beans and peas in your meals.

A typical day's menu might include...

BREAKFAST: Pancakes, oatmeal or a breakfast tortilla.

LUNCH: Vegetable soup, along with a vegetarian sandwich or a veggie burger.

DINNER: Bean burritos, mu-shu vegetables over rice, chili and rice, or spaghetti with marinara sauce, along with some fresh bread and a chickpea salad.

After a week or two on this diet, most people find themselves craving healthful foods—and not missing all that poisonous dietary fat.

CHOLESTEROL-LOWERING DRUGS...

With a high-risk patient—someone who's had a heart attack or appears headed for a heart attack, coronary bypass or angioplasty—I would not wait several months to "see what happens." If his/her total cholesterol hasn't fallen to 150 after 10 days of healthful eating, I suggest supplementing the diet with drugs.

Between a vegetarian diet and cholesterol-lowering medication, virtually anyone's cholesterol can be brought down to 150.

First, try natural cholesterol-lowering "medications"...

• ***Garlic*** (up to 800 milligrams [mg], or one clove a day).

• ***Oat bran*** (two ounces a day) or oatmeal (three ounces, dry weight, a day).

• ***Vitamin C*** (2,000 mg a day).

• ***Vitamin E*** (consult your doctor for amount).

• ***Beta-carotene*** (25,000 IU a day).

• ***Gugulipid*** (500 to 1,500 mg, three times a day).

• ***Immediate-release niacin*** is yet another potentially useful medication. But it can damage the liver, so it should be taken only under a doctor's supervision.

If the patient does not respond, I typically prescribe *simvastatin* (Zocor), *pravastatin* (Pravachol) or another statin drug. Since my patient may have to take this medication for years, it's important to match him with a drug that's effective and well-tolerated.

EXERCISE AND GOOD HABITS...

While exercise isn't as crucial as diet, a brisk walk of at least 20 minutes each day benefits your heart and arteries in many ways.

Exercise trains the heart to beat more efficiently...increases levels of HDL (good) cholesterol...lowers levels of triglycerides ...increases oxygen flow to your heart, brain, muscles and other tissues...and boosts the immune system.

AS IF YOU DIDN'T KNOW: Don't smoke. Drink alcohol moderately if at all. Limit coffee consumption (both regular and decaffeinated raise cholesterol levels about 10%). Your arteries will thank you.

■

THE OJ CONNECTION

Source: **John M. Miller, MD,** professor of medicine and director of clinical cardiac electrophysiology at Indiana University School of Medicine, Indianapolis.

Drinking orange juice every day may help prevent coronary disease.

NEW STUDY: Researchers examined the effects of drinking orange juice on the blood vessel function of 24 patients who had coronary disease. For two weeks, these patients, who had blood vessels narrowed by more than 50%, drank one of four different types of drinks—vitamin C–fortified juice drink, plain orange juice, vitamin C–fortified orange juice or orange juice fortified with vitamins C and E. All four types of drinks were tested on each person, with a two-week "washout" period of no juice between each two-week test period.

Drinking a glass of any type of orange juice twice each day significantly reduced both systolic and diastolic blood pressure. Drinking orange juice was associated with improvements in blood vessel function, as determined by flow-mediated dilation, a measure of the elasticity of the blood vessels.

IMPLICATION: Although these effects are minor compared with other heart disease risk factors, people who want to do everything possible to stay healthy should consider adding two eight-ounce glasses of orange juice to their daily diet.

■

STOP STROKES BEFORE THEY STRIKE

Source: **Gregory W. Albers, MD,** professor of neurology and neurological sciences at Stanford University Medical Center and director of the Stanford Stroke Center. He also is chairman of the American College of Chest Physicians' expert panel for both stroke and atrial fibrillation, cochairman of the National Stroke Association's Stroke Center Network and chairman of the American Heart Association's Metro Stroke Task Force.

Imagine opening the mail when suddenly your right arm feels weak and numb. You try to say something to your spouse but you cannot form the words. Then, as suddenly as your symptoms arrived, they disappear.

All too often, such fleeting symptoms are dismissed as fatigue or a pinched nerve. But in many cases, they signal a transient ischemic attack (TIA). Like strokes, TIAs are caused by a temporary interruption in blood flow to part of the brain. With these "ministrokes," however, the interruption is brief—usually lasting just minutes—and there is no permanent brain injury.

But a TIA is a *serious* warning. More than one-third of TIA patients go on to suffer a stroke within five years. Each year, more than 350,000 stroke patients become permanently disabled or die.

GOOD NEWS: TIAs can alert sufferers of the need for medication and other steps to prevent a full-blown stroke.

IDENTIFYING SYMPTOMS...

In addition to weakness on one side of the body (particularly in the arm, face or leg) and difficulty speaking, telltale TIA symptoms include unsteady gait...sudden vision loss or disturbance in one or both eyes...and/or dizziness or headache accompanied by any of the above symptoms.

Of course, these symptoms also characterize a stroke. Doctors have traditionally distinguished the two conditions by defining a TIA as an episode that lasts less than 24 hours and does not cause brain damage. However, that definition is being reconsidered.

We now know that any episode lasting longer than *one hour* is almost certain to progress to a brain-injuring stroke. Therefore, many stroke experts are pushing to redefine TIA as a nondamaging episode lasting less than one hour.

SCARY: Stroke patients have only a three-hour window during which they can receive a special clot-busting drug that may minimize or prevent permanent brain injury. Yet the average patient waits 12 to 24 hours before seeking medical attention.

WHAT TO DO: If symptoms persist for longer than five minutes, call 911. You may be suffering a full-blown stroke. If symptoms last less than five minutes, have someone drive you to a hospital emergency department to determine whether you've suffered a TIA.

TIA symptoms always warrant same-day medical attention. In a recent study, one out of 20 patients reporting to hospitals with a TIA suffered a subsequent stroke within 48 hours.

GETTING A DIAGNOSIS...

Once you arrive at the hospital emergency department, a physician should use ultrasound or another imaging technique to determine if there are blockages in major blood vessels, including your carotid (neck) arteries. If atherosclerotic plaque is clogging these arteries and narrowing (stenosis) of 70% or more is present, you're in danger of a stroke.

The doctor may recommend surgery (carotid endarterectomy) to remove the plaque. During this procedure, the surgeon makes a small incision just below the jaw to access the carotid artery and clean out the blockage.

The doctor should also perform an electrocardiogram (EKG) to check for atrial fibrillation, a type of irregular heartbeat that heightens the risk that blood clots will form in the heart and travel to the brain. If you have this condition, a prescription blood thinner, such as *warfarin* (Coumadin), can substantially reduce your stroke risk.

If your carotids are clear and your heart is beating normally, the doctor will likely start you on antiplatelet medication, such as aspirin, *clopidogrel* (Plavix) or *ticlopidine* (Ticlid). Excessively sticky platelets can clump together to form vessel-blocking clots. Aspirin and other antiplatelet drugs help prevent such clots.

The doctor will also test your blood pressure and cholesterol—two leading contributors to TIA and stroke.

HIGH BLOOD PRESSURE...

High blood pressure (hypertension) damages arteries, causing them to thicken and constrict. This compromises blood flow and puts you at risk for TIA and stroke.

How high is too high? While hypertension is usually defined as blood pressure of 140/90 or above, recent data suggest that readings of 120/80 or above may constitute a health hazard.

RECENT STUDY: Patients who had recently suffered a stroke were given either one or two blood pressure drugs or a placebo. Those patients receiving only an ACE inhibitor showed a minimal reduction in blood pressure and virtually no reduction in stroke risk. The patients given an ACE inhibitor plus a diuretic saw an 11-point drop in systolic blood pressure and a 40% reduction in stroke risk.

IMPORTANT: Some people—particularly those age 65 and older—may become dizzy or light-headed if blood pressure is 120/80 or below. In such cases, blood pressure may need to be slightly higher. Consult your doctor.

HIGH CHOLESTEROL...

A high level of low-density lipoprotein (LDL) "bad" cholesterol leads to plaque in your arteries, heightening your risk for TIA and stroke. The good news is that cholesterol-lowering "statin" drugs have been shown to substantially reduce stroke risk.

SELF-DEFENSE: TIA patients are advised to keep their LDL levels below 100. Your doctor can help you devise a cholesterol-lowering plan, including diet, exercise and/or statin drug therapy.

HEALTHY LIFESTYLE...

While drugs or surgery can alleviate some immediate stroke dangers following TIA, the real task of preventing future "brain attacks" falls to the patient.

In addition to eating a low-fat, low-cholesterol diet, maintaining a healthy weight and getting regular exercise, you should consider getting a blood test to check your homocysteine levels. Elevated levels of this amino acid (above 10) are associated with increased stroke and heart attack risk.

Folic acid lowers blood levels of homocysteine, with virtually no side effects. Trials now under way should determine whether reducing homocysteine levels decreases stroke and heart attack risk. In the meantime, I recommend that patients with elevated homocysteine take a folic acid supplement. Consult your doctor.

■

FLU VACCINE CUTS STROKE RISK

Source: **Pierre Amarenco, MD,** chairman, Neurology and Stroke Center, Denis Diderot University, Paris. His study was published in *Stroke.*

The flu vaccine cuts stroke risk in half—and even more in people who have received the vaccine for five consecutive years. The vaccine helps prevent influenza and resulting secondary infections, which cause inflammation. Inflammation is associated with atherosclerotic plaque buildup in the arteries, and a rupture of this plaque leads to stroke.

HOWEVER: The flu vaccine does not prevent stroke in people age 75 or older, perhaps because high blood pressure and other conditions override this protective effect.

SELF-DEFENSE: Speak to your doctor about receiving the flu shot every October, especially if you are in a high-risk group, such as those with a compromised immune system or asthma.

■

ALZHEIMER'S SELF-DEFENSE

Source: **Robert Sheeler, MD,** medical editor, *Mayo Clinic Health Letter,* 200 First St. SW, Rochester, MN 55905.

Vitamins E and C may ward off Alzheimer's. Two studies suggest that these antioxidants help prevent brain-cell damage by neutralizing toxic by-products in the body, helping to avert Alzheimer's. The benefits were seen as a result of a diet rich in these vitamins, but not from taking supplements.

Foods rich in vitamin E include grains, nuts, milk and egg yolks. Vitamin C is found in citrus fruits, broccoli and cabbage.

■

EASY WAYS TO REDUCE YOUR RISK OF ALZHEIMER'S

Source: **Robert Friedland, MD,** neurologist, laboratory of neurogeriatrics, department of neurology, Case Western Reserve University, University Hospitals of Cleveland.

Risk of developing Alzheimer's is sharply decreased by exercise—both physical and mental. A seven-year-long study of 2,000 people over age 65 found that those who engaged in high levels of reading, physical exercise or just talking with friends reduced their risk of Alzheimer's by 38%.

WHY: All physical and mental activities help increase blood flow to your brain, which strengthens its resistance to disease and increases connections among nerve cells. The brain is like any other organ in the body—it ages better, with better function, when it is used.

■

2 

AMERICA'S TOP 10 RETIREMENT BREAKTHROUGHS

IT'S NOT TOO LATE TO PUT YOUR RETIREMENT DREAMS BACK ON TRACK

Source: **Lee Rosenberg, CFP,** principal, ARS Financial Services, Inc., 500 N. Broadway, Jericho, NY 11753. A frequent guest on CNBC, Mr. Rosenberg is author of *Retirement: Ready or Not* (Career Press).

I can't make up for the money my clients have lost in the stock market. What I usually *can* do is put their retirement plans back on track by helping them see things in a new light. **HERE IS THE ADVICE I'M GIVING MY OLDER CLIENTS TODAY...**

• ***Stop treating your principal as sacred.*** When stock prices were soaring, the idea became widespread that retirees could live on investment gains, interest income and dividends. The principal would stay intact, to be passed along as bequests to children and grandchildren.

NEW REALITY: You shouldn't sabotage your own well-being so your children can inherit. All you owe your children is not to become a financial burden to them. You are not required to also leave them large sums of money.

You don't even have to spell this out in a formal session with your kids. They have suffered their own financial setbacks and thereby have more realistic expectations about what they can expect from their mom and dad. They understand their parents have endured investment losses that they probably won't live long enough to recoup.

Let the children know that you have enough resources to pay your own way...that you don't expect ever to call on them for help...and that you hope there still will be some inheritance for them down the road.

• ***Stop confusing luxuries with necessities.*** The better things became in the 1990s, the more luxuries came to be regarded as necessities. Older couples traveled extensively. They bought fancy new cars and designer wardrobes. Many began living as snowbirds, keeping the family home, but spending the cold winter months in a warmer climate.

My clients usually can save a lot of money by cutting back on travel, clothing and furnishings. Most couples can agree to keep the old car running longer. Instead of two homes, many now opt for one—and usually the less expensive one.

I often convince older couples to cut back on what they give to grandchildren. Given today's financial realities, funding a 529 college savings plan for even one grandchild can derail the grandparents' entire retirement plan.

• ***Decrease the volatility of your investments.*** Most people responded to the bull market by overemphasizing stocks in their portfolios. Retirees who once had, say, 50% in stocks and 50% in bonds, went to 75% or even 100% in stocks.

Today, I'm reducing the volatility of their portfolios by recommending an allocation of 30% stocks and 70% bonds. I point out that had they stuck to that allocation over the past five years, they would be in far better financial shape than they are today. That doesn't make up for the stock market losses they've already suffered. But it does start them on the path to financial recovery and it does let them sleep better at night. I'm steering clients to funds that emphasize conservative, low-volatility securities.

• ***If it doesn't pay income, don't invest in it.*** The assumption in the 1990s was that you could totally finance retirement by living on realized capital gains.

The lesson I drum into older clients today is, "Cash flow is king." Many of my clients are selling off any stock that doesn't pay a dividend.

TODAY'S CHOICES: To seek more income, my clients today are investing in real estate investment trusts (REITs), Government National Mortgage Association (Ginnie Mae) mutual funds, preferred stock and annuities. Investors in the higher tax brackets are choosing state-specific municipal bond funds, which are exempt from federal tax and state income tax.

• ***Tap the wealth in your home.*** It can be hard to convince retirees they should take out new loans against their homes. Most have paid off their mortgages and are relieved to own their homes free and clear.

REALITY: The value of real estate keeps increasing. You can overcome stock market losses and finance a very comfortable retirement by tapping into the wealth that has accumulated in your home. **HOW...**

• Borrow against your house. If your mortgage is paid off, you may be able to take out a sizable amount in cash through a home-equity loan or another mortgage.

• Trade down. A married couple can take $500,000 in profit out of a home tax free. Sell the home at today's inflated prices, and buy something cheaper and more suitable. You not only gain enough to fatten your retirement nest egg, but you may end up with a house that is easier to maintain—and easier for older people to live in.

• Sell your house and then rent somewhere else. That way, you can take all your equity out of the home—providing lots of cash to live on in retirement.

• ***Revise your retirement vision.*** I have many clients who had expected to be retired by now, but who are staying on the job until their retirement funds are replenished.

And I have many clients who are retired, but have taken on part-time jobs to flesh out their retirement savings. One client makes $25,000 a year working part-time in his son's business. Another makes $200 a day driving for a limo service on weekends. Still another now works as a freelance ad salesman at a local newspaper.

They find the work mentally stimulating as well as financially rewarding. Most important, they've found a way to help get their retirement plans back on track.

■

HOW TO CUT BACK AND SAVE FOR RETIREMENT

Source: **Jonathan Pond,** president, Financial Planning Information Inc., 1 Gateway Center, Newton, MA 02458. He is author of *Your Money Matters* (Putnam).

In addition to pouring money into retirement plans, here are several other smart ways to save for retirement...

• ***Consider canceling life insurance policies*** once your nest egg is large enough. Once your net worth grows to the point at which you have savings to cover emergencies and you have no more financial dependents, you may not need life insurance. At the very least, you can reduce the amount of your coverage.

• ***Invest in several rental real estate properties*** and devise a plan to pay off the mortgages by the time you retire. Once the mortgages are no longer a factor, you will have a dependable, increasing income stream with minimal expenses for your retirement. If you don't want to be bothered with the property management duties once you've retired, hire someone else to do it. Your cash flow will still be substantial.

• ***Develop sensible car-ownership habits.*** If you routinely keep each of your cars for 10 years instead of three, you'll save well over $100,000 during your working life.

• ***Consider the long-term impact of modifying everyday habits.***

EXAMPLE: Save at least $7 a day by eating breakfast at home and brown-bagging your lunch during the week. Do this for 25 years, investing the savings at 8.5%, and you'll save more than $100,000.

• ***Finally, beware of early retirement incentive packages*** if you haven't amassed a sizable nest egg. Many people have agreed to these incentives only to discover several years later that they really couldn't afford early retirement. Before accepting an incentive plan to retire, always compare what you would get under the plan with what you would get if you stayed for a few more years.

EXAMPLE: At some companies, a person retiring at age 59 might receive 60% less per year in pension money than someone retiring at age 65.

The company is betting it will save money because you will probably live a long time in retirement. That's what the actuarial tables tell them, and these tables are fairly accurate.

■

RETIREMENT ABROAD

Source: **Kenneth A. Stern, CFP,** president, Asset Planning Solutions, San Diego, CA. He is author of *50 Fabulous Places to Retire in America* (Career Press).

If you do not mind a major culture change and really want to stretch your retirement dollars, consider moving abroad...

• ***Mexico.*** Some of the places now attracting an increasing number of Americans include Tijuana, comfortably close to San Diego...and Rosarito, about 200 miles down the Pacific coastline. One thousand miles further south is Puerto Vallarta, a charming coastal resort.

• ***Costa Rica.*** San José, the country's capital, has a lot to offer, including a climate milder than Florida's, the lowest crime rate of any foreign community that's popular among US expatriates and friendly people—most of whom speak English.

• ***The Bahamas.*** Nassau, a tropical paradise, is now an offshore banking haven attracting a growing number of retirees. You don't need to worry about learning a new language in this English-speaking nation.

THE RELOCATION DECISION...

Even if a particular community seems ideal at first sight, whether it's abroad or in the US, do not buy until you have spent time there on several occasions—and during different seasons. If it still appeals to you, rent for a year before you buy a new home, to be sure you are in the right place.

■

SMART WAYS TO TAP INTO YOUR RETIREMENT NEST EGG

Source: **Ronald Yolles,** attorney and chartered financial analyst, Yolles-Samrah Investment Management, Inc., 33 Bloomfield Hills Parkway, Bloomfield Hills, MI 48304. He is coauthor of *You're Retired, Now What? Money Skills for a Comfortable Retirement* and *Getting Started in Retirement Planning* (both from Wiley).

Many people spend all of their working lives building up retirement savings accounts—and then make one of two devastating mistakes when they withdraw their money from those accounts.

- ***They withdraw too much too soon***—leaving their retirement funds badly eroded somewhere down the line.
- ***They withdraw too little too late***—leaving a big estate to their children, but pinching pennies while still alive.

HOW TO HANDLE WITHDRAWALS...

- ***Start your withdrawal planning today.*** What throws some people off track is thinking that they should be planning for retirement, when they really should be planning to maintain financial independence.

RESULT: They start taking withdrawals from their retirement accounts on the date that they retire, whether they need to or not.

Retirement is only a date on a calendar. It doesn't mean that all of your income immediately dries up and you are instantly forced to tap into your nest egg—you only do that when you must to maintain your lifestyle.

IMPORTANT: When you are working, your financial independence comes from the salary you earn. When you retire, it comes from your pension, Social Security benefits and, perhaps, income from a postretirement job.

Withdraw from your retirement savings accounts only when other sources of income fall short and you need that money in order to remain financially independent.

- ***Calculate how much income you will need in retirement.*** That is where people really can get into trouble. They use a formula from a broker or a financial magazine that says they can get by on 60% or 70% of preretirement income. They build their withdrawal strategy around that magic number.

REALITY: There is no such thing today as a "standard" retirement and no magic number to tell you how much you will need in retirement.

Recently, a colleague and I interviewed more than 100 people and found almost no one who was retiring in the traditional sense of retirement—doing a little gardening, playing a little golf. People are staying incredibly active well into their 70s and 80s—traveling more, buying second homes, working at postretirement jobs and/or volunteering.

Your spending could go down when you retire, but just as easily it could go up because you are traveling more and helping the kids with their expenses.

• ***Don't rely on any magic number.*** **PREPARE A BUDGET THAT REPRESENTS YOUR BEST GUESS ABOUT ALL YOUR EXPENSES IN RETIREMENT...**

• How much will you travel?

• Will you help a child buy a home?

• Are you planning to pay for one (or more) grandchild's education?

• Will you work after retirement...and how much can you realistically expect to earn?

Consider the first year or two of your retirement as a period of testing and learning. Then take another look at the budget and adjust it as necessary.

• ***Delay withdrawals until the last possible minute.*** Every day that you delay taking withdrawals from your retirement plans —IRAs and 401(k)—is yet another day that tax-sheltered compounding keeps your retirement savings growing.

STRATEGY: If you can, wait until age 70½ to begin making withdrawals. That's when the law says you must start. If you can't wait that long—wait until you really need the money.

• ***Before you tap tax-sheltered accounts,*** withdraw from your taxable investment accounts. Doing so preserves tax sheltering for as long as possible.

Gains in taxable accounts are taxed at the capital gains rate (maximum 15%). All withdrawals from tax-sheltered accounts are taxed as ordinary income (maximum 35%). Hang on to that tax advantage as long as it is possible.

• ***When you start withdrawing,*** withdraw the minimum. Even if you wait till age 70½ to start withdrawals, withdraw the minimum that's allowed by law.

HELPFUL: Calculating the allowable minimum withdrawal is complicated, so you'll probably want some help from an attorney, CPA or financial planner.

Under IRS rules, the minimum distribution incidental benefit (MDIB) method is used to calculate the minimum withdrawals. This uses the joint life expectancy of the IRA owner and a hypothetical person 10 years younger than the owner as the period over which distributions must be taken.

KEY: This method is used even if there's no beneficiary or the beneficiary is not 10 years younger.

EXCEPTION: IRA owners who have a spouse more than 10 years younger than themselves can calculate the required distributions over their actual joint life expectancies—which will work even better than using the MDIB method.

• ***Make the most of Social Security.*** The one exception to the last-minute approach to withdrawals applies to Social Security.

You can get a bigger payout by waiting until your normal retirement age (e.g., 65 and six months for those born in 1940).

OUR ADVICE: Don't wait. Take the money as early as possible, especially if you're not working—at age 62 if you can. We have worked through scenarios for hundreds of clients. In more than 90% of the cases, it makes sense to start Social Security payments as early as possible, instead of waiting for a bigger payout down the road.

• ***Include investment planning in your retirement planning.*** The most overlooked aspect of withdrawal planning is how to alter your approach to investing when you start to make significant withdrawals.

The need for growth investments doesn't change when you retire. With people living longer, the best strategy is to continue to invest heavily in common stocks for their superior long-term-growth potential. But once you start withdrawing from retirement accounts, market volatility will become your enemy. You need to dampen it as much as possible.

REASON: The money for withdrawals comes from selling the investments in your retirement accounts. The more you must sell in a down market, the quicker you'll go through your retirement nest egg.

Since 1926, 24% of the five-year periods in the stock market have produced returns that were either negative or lower than the return on fixed-income investments. That's too risky, once you begin taking withdrawals.

STRATEGY: Dampen the volatility by shifting more of your retirement accounts into bonds.

Until retirement, I advise keeping your allocation 70% stocks, 25% bonds and 5% cash. Once you begin withdrawing from retirement savings, shift to 50% stocks, 40% bonds and 10% cash.

■

HOW TO TAKE EARLY PENALTY-FREE WITHDRAWALS FROM RETIREMENT PLANS

Source: **James Blinka, CPA,** tax partner, BDO Seidman, LLP, Two Plaza E., 330 E. Kilbourn Ave., Milwaukee, WI 53202.

Anyone who withdraws money from an IRA or other tax-deferred retirement plan will owe income tax, assuming the account was funded with deductible contributions.

In most situations, you will also owe a 10% penalty tax on any withdrawals before age 59½. For example, if you take out $10,000 at age 54 (and don't qualify for any exception to the penalty), you would have to pay a $1,000 penalty.

But there are some exceptions to the early withdrawal penalty. If you really must take an early withdrawal, use one of the following methods to avoid the 10% penalty tax bite.

UNIVERSAL EXCEPTIONS...

The following exceptions apply to all tax-deferred retirement plans...

• ***Death.*** If you inherit a retirement account, you won't face the 10% penalty. That's true no matter how old you are (and no matter how old the participant was at the time of death).

• ***Disability.*** Again, the 10% penalty does not apply if you cannot work and need to make a withdrawal.

How can you prove to the IRS that you are disabled? In most cases, you should be receiving disability checks from Social Security or from an insurance policy.

SMART 1040 STRATEGY: Attach an explanation to your tax return, clearly stating that you are receiving disability benefits and that the 10% penalty should not apply.

• ***Medical bills.*** The 10% penalty will not apply to money spent for deductible medical expenses in excess of 7.5% of your adjusted gross income (AGI).

• ***Substantially equal periodic payments (SEPPs).*** Avoid the 10% penalty by withdrawing annual amounts based on your life expectancy. These payments must continue for at least five years or until age 59½, whichever comes later.

CAUTION: If you don't maintain the SEPPs until the later of five years or until age 59½, you will owe the 10% penalty tax on all withdrawals, retroactively.

EMPLOYER-SPONSORED PLANS...

The following two exceptions to the 10% early withdrawal penalty apply only to withdrawals from 401(k)s, profit-sharing plans and other qualified retirement plans.

• ***Separation from service.*** If you leave your employer, you can take money from your retirement account and not pay a penalty.

REQUIREMENT: The separation must occur no earlier than the year you reach age 55.

• ***Qualified domestic relations orders (QDROs).*** In a divorce or marital separation, a QDRO is an order to the plan administrator to transfer part of one spouse's account to the other spouse. Such a transfer won't be subject to tax. But subsequent withdrawals from an employer-sponsored plan under a QDRO before age 59½ will be subject to a penalty.

IMPLICATION: You can give or receive alimony or child support from an employer-sponsored retirement plan, penalty free, as long as those payments are required by a QDRO.

Don't take the money out of a plan and then give it to your spouse. The IRS will look harshly on that approach, applying income tax under the theory that you took a distribution. Money should go directly to the beneficiary of the QDRO, as required.

IRA EXCEPTIONS...

The separation-from-service and QDRO exceptions do not apply to early distributions from IRAs. **ON THE OTHER HAND, THERE ARE ESCAPE HATCHES THAT ARE ONLY FOR IRAs...**

• ***Higher education.*** Distributions from IRAs to pay post-high-school expenses are exempt from the 10% penalty.

ELIGIBLE EXPENSES: Tuition, room and board, fees, books, supplies and necessary equipment.

These qualifying expenses can be used to pay for your education or that of your spouse, your children or your grandchildren.

• ***Health insurance.*** After you are out of work for 12 consecutive weeks, you can take money from an IRA to keep your health insurance in force, penalty free.

After you're back at work, you won't owe a penalty on IRA withdrawals used to pay health insurance premiums for the next 60 days.

• ***Purchasing a first home.*** You may take penalty-free withdrawals up to $10,000 for a first-time home purchase.

REQUIRED: You cannot have had an ownership interest in a residence during the previous two years. The $10,000 is a lifetime limit.

ROTH IRAs...

If you're withdrawing money before age 59½ from a Roth IRA converted from a traditional IRA, you'll owe the penalty on the amount that is attributable to your earnings inside the Roth IRA, but not to your original contributions.

EXCEPTIONS: Death, disability and first-time home buyer up to $10,000.

THE SEPP SOLUTION...

Some of the exceptions listed above (death, disability, divorce) apply only in specific circumstances. However, IRA owners can make use of the SEPP exception at any time. Participants in other plans can use SEPPs after separation from service.

SEPP rules are so flexible that you can take out almost any amount needed, penalty free, as long as your account balance is large enough. **THREE METHODS PERMITTED BY THE IRS...**

• ***Life expectancy.*** You withdraw money which is based on your life expectancy, according to the IRS tables. For instance, if your life expectancy is 40 years, you would calculate 1/40 (2.5%) of your plan balance and withdraw that much each year.

• ***Amortization.*** You calculate that your initial plan balance will grow by a reasonable rate, perhaps 6% or 7% per year. The higher the assumed rate is, the greater the penalty-free withdrawals permitted. This method allows much higher withdrawals than the life-expectancy method.

• ***Annuitization.*** This complicated calculation, incorporating annuity factors and present values, allows you to withdraw a bit more than with the amortization method.

EXAMPLE: You have a $600,000 IRA and you wish to withdraw $2,500 per month. However, if the SEPP rules (amortization method) require that you withdraw $3,750 each month from a $600,000 IRA, you'd be paying tax on an unneeded $1,250 a month.

SOLUTION: Split your $600,000 IRA into a $400,000 IRA and a $200,000 IRA, tax free. Then take distributions from the $400,000 IRA, pulling out the $2,500 per month that you need, using the amortization method. In your other $200,000 IRA, you can continue the tax-free buildup.

■

MAKE YOUR HEIRS RICH: NO COST TO YOU

Source: **Irving L. Blackman, CPA,** founding partner, Blackman Kallick Bartelstein, LLP, 10 S. Riverside Plaza, Chicago 60606, *www.taxsecretsofthewealthy.com.*

If you want to make a major bequest to a child or grandchild, the smart way to do it may be to use life insurance instead of a bequest of property.

Say you want to leave $1 million to a grandchild. First you need to have at least that much in assets—and, after federal and local estate taxes, you may need twice as much. Remember, federal estate tax isn't scheduled to be repealed until 2010 and may never be—and state death taxes continue to apply.

Also, income earned on the assets is subject to income tax at top rates—and the assets are "tied up." You can't spend them *and* bequeath them, too. If you wish to make several such bequests, these problems are multiplied.

ALTERNATIVE: Fund the bequest to the child with a $1 million life insurance policy held in a life insurance trust. **WHY...**

• ***A properly structured trust will be estate tax free***—reducing the assets you need by as much as half and cutting the IRS out.

• ***Investment income*** earned within the insurance policy will be tax free.

• ***The dollar cost is very low*** since the value of the policy is leveraged through tax savings.

EXAMPLE: A married couple, both age 60, find they can buy a $1 million second-to-die life insurance policy (that pays on the death of the survivor) for an annual premium of about $13,000 a year for 15 years. They place the policy in a life insurance trust benefiting a child. Policy premiums are gift tax free, due to the couple's annual joint gift tax exclusion ($22,000 in 2005).

PAYOFF: The child will receive $1 million tax free at a maximum cash cost to the couple of only $195,000. And the after-tax cost may be as much as 50% less, as the $195,000 is removed from their taxable estate.

■

TAX HELP FOR YOUR PARENTS

Source: **Alan S. Zipp, Esq., CPA,** 932 Hungerford Dr., Rockville, MD 20850. Mr. Zipp is an instructor of tax courses for the American Institute of CPAs.

Your parents (or one parent) may want to stay in the house where they've lived for years—but may also need to tap their home equity in order to live comfortably.

You can help them out by buying the home and then renting it back to them. You enjoy the tax benefits of owning investment property, in addition to deductions for mortgage interest and property taxes. Your parents will have cash to support their lifestyle as well as the opportunity to stay in their home.

Your parents may have run out of home-owners' tax breaks...

• ***If they've been in the house for many years,*** the mortgage may be paid off, or nearly paid off. As the owners, they might be getting little or no deductions for mortgage interest.

• ***Any mortgage interest or property tax deductions*** your parents now take may have very little value, if they're in a low tax bracket in retirement.

• ***Your parents (like many seniors) may not even itemize deductions***—so they'd be getting no tax benefit from home ownership.

But a sale-leaseback presents your parents and you with substantial new tax breaks.

TAX-FREE GAINS...

It's often better for one child rather than a group of children to buy the house from the parents. This helps reduce disputes among the siblings and other complications. A fair value should be paid for the house—to avoid hard feelings among the other children.

LOOPHOLE: Home owners (your parents) can sell a principal residence and avoid tax on up to $500,000 worth of gain, if a joint tax return is filed. Single filers can avoid tax on up to $250,000 worth of gain.

If a sale-leaseback is arranged so that the profit falls under the $250,000 or $500,000 limit, no capital gains tax will be due.

EXAMPLE: Nancy White, a widow with a basis of $200,000 in her house, might sell it to her son, Dan White, for $450,000 without triggering any tax. Then Nancy can live in the house indefinitely, paying rent to Dan.

The IRS might claim that the house was undervalued and that the difference was a taxable gift. In the above example, the IRS might argue that the house was really worth $600,000 at the time of sale, so Nancy gave Dan a gift of $150,000—the $600,000 value of the house minus the $450,000 selling price.

SELF-DEFENSE: To demonstrate the value of a house at the time of the sale, collect current newspaper listings, showing asking prices of similar homes.

For extra protection against an IRS attack, get a professional appraisal to support the price actually paid. With the amount of tax money at stake, an independent appraisal is cheap insurance.

Another good way to reduce your exposure to an IRS challenge is to indicate that the sale-leaseback resulted in a small gift. This tactic may block an audit.

In the previous example, where the selling price was $450,000, Nancy could file a gift tax return, explaining that she made an $11,000 gift to her son because the house was worth $461,000.

To avoid IRS complications, attach an explanation and documentation available to support the value placed on the house.

If you report a small gift, keep in mind that gifts of up to $11,000 a year ($22,000 joint) are free of gift tax.

AUDIT FREE: Under current tax law, the IRS has only three years to audit a gift tax return and challenge a valuation, provided the gift has been adequately disclosed. If you get by the three-year limit, you won't have to worry about a challenge far in the future.

FAIR DEALING...

To claim the tax benefits of owning investment property, your parents must pay you a fair rent.

You can even give your parents a break on "fair market value" rent by charging less. You can do this because when renting to relatives, you will likely realize savings in maintenance and management fees.

Suppose that the house is in a neighborhood where similar houses rent for $1,000 per month. You can rent the house to your parents for $800 per month—a 20% discount—and still claim the tax benefits.

TRAP: If the rent is too low, the IRS can say that your parents' stay in the house is personal use for you, the new owner. In that case, tax benefits will be limited to deductions for property taxes and mortgage interest—the same as they would be if you used the property as a vacation home.

As long as the rent is fair and the house is considered rental property, however, you also can take deductions for depreciation and operating expenses—utilities, maintenance, insurance, repairs, supplies, etc.

Travel expenses also may be deductible. If you go to visit your rental property, some or even all of your expenses can be written off as investment property monitoring—but the deductions must be reasonable in relation to the income generated by the property.

BONUS: Residential properties placed in service can be depreciated over 27.5 years.

You *can't* depreciate the cost of the property allocated to land. Be sure the house sale comes with an appraisal allocating the price paid for depreciable improvements.

If you provide new furnishings and appliances, you can depreciate those items separately over a shorter time period.

WINNING FROM LOSSES...

All of these deductions can offset the rental income you receive from your parents. Therefore, most or even all of this income can be tax sheltered.

Your deductions might even exceed the rental income, generating a loss that may be deductible, in whole or in part, if your adjusted gross income (AGI) is less than $150,000.

LIMITATION: In general, you can deduct your losses up to $25,000 per year, as long as your AGI is less than $100,000. As your AGI exceeds that, your ability to deduct losses is reduced, dwindling to zero when your AGI reaches $150,000.

Suspended (unused) passive losses eventually can be deducted when the house is sold.

If you buy your parents' home for cash, and thus take no interest deduction, your income from the property may exceed deductions—so "passive" income will be generated.

Passive losses—such as unusable losses from old tax shelters—can offset this passive income.

EXIT STRATEGIES...

Aside from all the tax and financial consequences, other factors need to be taken into consideration with a sale-leaseback. You should sign a lease with your parents, as you would with any other tenant.

The lease might state that your parents are responsible for the routine maintenance of the house...and for preserving its marketability. Putting the terms of the agreement on paper will help if disputes arise.

Eventually, your parents no longer will be able to live in the house. At that point, you can sell it, rent to another tenant or move in. After you've lived there at least two years, you'll qualify for another $250,000 or $500,000 capital gains exclusion on a subsequent sale.

■

WILL YOU HAVE ENOUGH TO RETIRE?

Source: **Jonathan Pond,** president, Financial Planning Information Inc., 1 Gateway Center, Newton, MA 02458. He is author of *Your Money Matters* (Putnam).

Despite all the warnings about the need to save, many Americans still believe that the cost of retirement will be only 35% of their current income. The majority of the 80,000 adults I have surveyed are dangerously underestimating their future financial needs.

REALITY: Middle- and upper-income Americans require at least 80% of their preretirement income during retirement. You won't be paying payroll taxes, such as Social Security, or job-related expenses. And, of course, you won't have to save for retirement. But these reductions often are offset by your medical or travel costs. Also, if you have a large mortgage, your expenses could even exceed 80%.

TO PLAN SENSIBLY...

• ***Project your retirement budget.*** In my survey, only 23% of people age 50 and older actually had tried to estimate their retirement spending. Yet people in this age group *should* have well-developed retirement plans.

The calculation is simple. Base your projection on the assumption that you will live to be 95. If you plan for a shorter life expectancy, you risk running out of money. **FOR A QUICK ESTIMATE, FOLLOW THESE STEPS...**

• Take your current net income, and subtract the amount you are putting into savings. If, for example, you make $60,000 a year after taxes and save $10,000, then you are spending $50,000 a year.

• Multiply that figure—$50,000—by 80%, which is the percentage of current income you'll need in retirement. In this particular example, you would need $40,000 each year.

• Multiply $40,000 by the number of years between your retirement age and 95. If you plan to retire at age 65, that would be 30 years.

RESULT: You would need approximately $1.2 million to fund your retirement wisely.

I use current spending in this calculation with no adjustment for future inflation. I assume that inflation will average 3% a year and return on your nest egg will grow at least in line with inflation.

For a more exact estimate, use one of the free Internet tools. **MY FAVORITES...**

• *www.asec.org,* from American Savings Education Council. Click on "Savings Tools," then on "The Ballpark Estimate."

• *www.smartmoney.com/retirement.* Click on "The SmartMoney Retirement Worksheets" link.

• ***Project your retirement income.*** Not all that $1.2 million must come from your savings. Social Security and your pension, if you will receive one, will pay some of it.

• Find out what your Social Security benefit will be. The Social Security Administration (SSA) mails you an estimate each year around your birthday. Or you can request the statement anytime by contacting the SSA at 800-772-1213 or *www.socialsecurity.gov.*

• If you will have a pension, ask your employer's benefits department to estimate your future payment. Also ask what options you have for receiving benefits.

• Ask a representative at the financial services company that now manages your 401(k) plan to help you calculate how much money you eventually will accumulate and how much income it will generate.

• Assume that your other investments will appreciate until retirement—but be conservative. I now estimate a 6% return.

CLOSING THE GAP...

What if your calculation shows that you won't have enough money for retirement? **STEPS YOU CAN TAKE NOW...**

• ***Put your current expenses on a diet.*** I frequently see even high-income people with anemic nest eggs spending about 85% to 90% of their incomes.

Debt is substantially higher for most people than it was only a few years ago, according to my survey. Money used to pay off debt is lost to your retirement nest egg.

Starting now, begin paying down your debt—and stop adding to it.

• ***Delay retirement.*** If you work for just one year past your hoped-for retirement age—even without adding to your savings—you increase the amount you can draw from your nest egg over the rest of your life by 10%. This is based on the compounded growth of your investment and having fewer years to spend it.

• ***Break the lock*** on locked-in assets. My study shows that half of most people's wealth is tied up in their homes and their possessions. In California, that figure is closer to 60%. Owning a home may make you feel wealthy, but it doesn't provide retirement income.

WHAT TO DO: Pay off high-interest loans. Then devise a plan to pay off your mortgage as soon as possible in order to minimize interest payments. When the nest empties out, sell your home and buy something more modest. Add the profit to your nest egg.

CAUTION: Don't make extra mortgage payments until you can maximize your retirement-savings payments. Hopefully, you can do both. Even small extra payments help pay off the mortgage sooner.

EXAMPLE: If you have a $100,000 mortgage balance that runs for another 25 years, you can pay it off in just 15 years if you add $100 to each mortgage payment.

Couples can take up to $500,000 in capital gains from the sale of a house without owing taxes. That's a tremendous incentive to sell your home and find someplace less expensive to live. The amount of money you save could be substantial.

WHAT I ADVISE MY CLIENTS: Buy a two-bedroom apartment. With the money you save, you will be able to put the kids up in the most expensive hotel in town whenever they visit.

KEEP YOUR NEST EGG SAFE...

Many retirees take absurd risks in pursuit of high returns.

EXAMPLE: A retired couple I know lost almost 70% of their nest egg because they invested heavily in technology stocks. Now they have to sell their house, eliminate vacations and curtail daily living expenses just to make ends meet.

The best allocation to earn a 6% return is the classic 60% in stocks and 40% in bonds, no matter what your age.

After several bear market years, many retirees are horrified by the idea of having 60% of their assets in stocks. But they don't need just income—they need *growing* income. And growth in income only comes from stocks.

Here's how I would invest the 60% equity allocation...

- ***20% in large-cap value.***
- ***15% in large-cap growth.***
- ***15% in small- and mid-cap.***
- ***10% in international stock funds.***

■

YOU'RE NOT TOO OLD FOR LIFE INSURANCE

Source: **Terence L. Reed, CFP,** Livonia, MI. He is author of *The 8 Biggest Mistakes People Make with Their Finances Before and After Retirement* (Dearborn).

Seniors often assume that life insurance is only for families with young children. In fact, life insurance can be a great tool for seniors.

If you are in your 50s, you might pay $50,000 for a single-premium variable life insurance policy that carries a $100,000 death benefit. By doing so, you have *doubled* the effects of your retirement funds overnight.

Also, purchase life insurance to provide for a child with special needs...or to pay final medical expenses, which can be huge. If you don't have long-term-care insurance, use life insurance to protect your estate against Medicaid recoupment programs.

BIG RISK: If a nursing home stay exhausts your financial resources (other than exempt assets, such as a home), Medicaid will pick up the tab. At your death, the federal government may go after what is left of your estate to recover the bills Medicaid paid. Without money to reimburse Medicaid, your spouse could face losing the family home.

■

3 

CREDIT CARD SECRETS: WHAT BANKS DON'T WANT YOU TO KNOW

CREDIT CARD TRAPS

Source: Bottom Line's Smart Consumer: How to Get the Best Deals, Anytime, Anywhere (Bottom Line Books).

Because of intense competition, credit card issuers are trying to lure you in with the flashiest and most irresistible introductory teaser APRs, consumer perks and rebates. There are some tremendous deals to be found out there, but don't be taken in the process.

Credit cards can be damaging to your budget if you forget that carrying a balance is the same as borrowing money—at an unusually high rate of interest.

DIFFERENT CARDS FOR DIFFERENT CUSTOMERS...

Shop around for the credit card terms that best suit your budget and repayment style. For instance, if you routinely pay your bills in full each month, focus on the amount of the annual fee and other charges.

If you will be paying your credit card debt off slowly, however, shop for a low APR and consider how your issuer calculates finance charges. In either case, your costs will be affected by whether or not the company offers a grace period.

Here are some key issues to consider…

- ***Annual percentage rate (APR).***
- ***Cash-advance fees.***
- ***Annual fee.***
- ***Late-payment charges.***
- ***Grace period.***
- ***Over-the-limit fees.***

ELITE CARDS: Elite cards, such as the Visa Signature card and the World MasterCard, are giving American Express a run for its money. Some of these cards offer enticing perks, such as guaranteed airport parking, air-miles reward programs that can be applied to most airlines, special services at luxury hotels and VIP access to special events.

While they don't offer advantages as comprehensive as the advantages offered to American Express Platinum cardholders, Visa and MasterCard issues tend to be less expensive—with lower annual fees than American Express, depending on the issuer. Visa Signature cards and World MasterCards also have no preset spending limits and sometimes low APRs. Terms and fees vary from issuer to issuer.

REBATE CARDS: A lot of credit card issuers are scaling down or eliminating costly rebate programs. Still, there are some excellent programs out there that provide a way to accumulate air miles or give you a rebate on your next car purchase. But beware of the high APRs more and more frequently associated with the rebate cards. These cards can be a great value only if you pay your balance off promptly. A large balance carried month to month can easily cancel out any benefits of the rebate.

DEBT CONSOLIDATION: If you have a lot of credit card debt spread over different cards, consider consolidating it on one low-rate card. Card issuers supply courtesy or convenience checks, or balance-transfer forms to pay off your other cards (although sometimes with hefty transfer fees). Make sure that the low interest rate on your new card lasts long enough to pay off your debt. Switching your debt from card to card looks bad on your credit rating.

PLASTIC NOT-SO-FANTASTIC...

Hard to believe, perhaps, but many card issuers are actually looking for ways to trip you up. Interest rates are swelling and grace periods shrinking. Make one or two late payments and you might be socked with a higher interest rate, not to mention a late charge of $25 or more. Some issuers are levying penalties if a payment is even a day or two late. Also, the annual fees associated with cards are as much as $35 or higher in some cases.

Even if you pay off your balance within the grace period, banks will sometimes find ways to sneak in extra charges. If you pay your balance off like clockwork, look out for clauses concerning "inactivity" or "account closing fees" in your cardholder agreement. If you keep a zero balance and have a history of good credit, your card issuer may even find ways of penalizing you for your exemplary behavior. Remember, card issuers like customers who keep high balances on their credit cards. This is how they make money. Indeed, they may even deny you rewards, cancel your account or deny your application if your credit rating is too high.

Whatever you do, do not forget to read the fine print on credit card applications, cardholder agreements and correspondence from your credit card company. Big traps lie hidden in tiny type.

■

CREDIT CARD BILLING DATES DO MATTER

Source: **Gerri Detweiler,** president, Ultimate Credit Solutions, Inc., Sarasota, FL, and author of *Invest in Yourself: Six Secrets to a Rich Life* (Wiley).

If you have many bills due at the start of the month, ask your credit card issuers to bill you on a date that coordinates with when you receive your paycheck. And, know what your credit card's closing cycle is. You can then make a major purchase right after that month's closing date and have almost two months to pay, with no interest.

EXAMPLE: If your card cycle closes on the 15th, make a major purchase on the 16th. It will appear on the following month's bill, and you will then have an additional grace period before payment is due.

NOTE: This will only work if you pay your credit card bills in full each month and don't carry a balance.

■

EASY WAYS TO PAY OFF DEBTS

Source: **Mary Hunt,** editor, *Debt-Proof Living,* Box 2135, Paramount, CA 90723, *www.debtproofliving.com.*

How to pay off your debts without increasing the amount you have to pay each month...

- ***Stop incurring new debt.*** If you do not stop buying on credit, you will never pay off your debts.
- ***Total up all of your current monthly required minimum payments*** on all your debts and credit cards. Commit to paying this total amount each month until all your debts are paid off.
- ***List your debts in order of the number of months it will take to pay them.*** Put the shortest-term debts at the top of the list.
- ***When the shortest-term debt is paid off,*** add the amount that you paid on it each month to the amount that you're paying on the next-shortest-term debt.
- ***When the second debt is paid off,*** add the amount that you paid on the first two debts to what you pay on the third debt ...and so on.

■

BANKRUPTCY ALTERNATIVES

For those considering bankruptcy, this easy-to-understand Web site gives alternatives—*www.debtworkout.com.*

■

BEST WAYS TO FIX CREDIT-REPORT PROBLEMS

Source: **Eric Gertler,** a nationally recognized expert on privacy, data transfer and identity theft, is the author of *Prying Eyes* (Random House).

If you have proof that an item on your credit report is not correct, contact the creditor or lender. Every creditor is required under the federal Fair Credit Reporting Act to send updates to credit-reporting agencies, usually within 30 days.

In a letter, state the disputed item, how it is inaccurate and how it should be fixed. Always include your full name and account number and copies of original documents. Send correspondence *return receipt requested.*

If you can't resolve a problem with a lender or creditor, get a copy of your credit report from the reporting agencies...

- ***Equifax,*** 800-685-1111, *www.equifax.com.*
- ***Experian,*** 888-397-3742, *www.experian.com.*
- ***TransUnion,*** 800-916-8800, *www.tuc.com.*

It is easiest to send written documentation of the inaccuracy to one of the credit-reporting agencies. It will make changes to your report if its investigation proves you correct. The other agencies will eventually pick up the corrected information, but to ensure prompt correction, contact all agencies directly.

Ask the agencies to send your corrected report to every company that received an inaccurate report in the past six months (or two years for employers who have requested your credit report).

If you can't resolve a disputed item, write up an explanation of up to 100 words. The credit agency should make this part of your file. If you believe a creditor or credit-reporting agency has not responded fairly or promptly to your situation, contact the Federal Trade Commission at 877-382-4357 or *www.ftc.gov.*

CAUTION: Steer clear of credit-repair companies that guarantee to "clean up" your credit report—they cannot. By law, negative information may be removed only if it is inaccurate or the reporting period—seven years or, in the case of bankruptcy, 10 years—has expired.

■

SHREWD WAYS TO PROTECT YOUR ASSETS AGAINST A LAWSUIT

Source: **Gideon Rothschild, Esq., CPA,** a partner in the law firm Moses & Singer LLP, 1301 Avenue of the Americas, New York City 10019, *www.mosessinger.com.*

We really do live in a litigious society. Even if you've done nothing wrong, you could find yourself the target of a ruinous lawsuit. But if you act *before* anyone sues, you can protect your assets. The sooner you act, the more options you have.

YOUR HOLDINGS...

Look to see where you are most vulnerable to a lawsuit. These areas should be the focus of your asset-protection strategy. **CONSIDER...**

• ***Your business interests.*** To what extent are your personal assets vulnerable as a result of you owning and/or running a business? Have you personally guaranteed any of your corporation's debts?

STRATEGY: If you are a general partner of a business, consider transforming that ownership interest into a limited liability company (LLC). Having the LLC act as the general partner will protect your personal assets.

• ***Your personal life.*** To what extent are you personally vulnerable as a result of your marital status? If you are married, what impact would divorce have on your assets? Be sure to consider state property rights (such as community property), prenuptial agreements and other arrangements.

BEWARE: The wealthier you are, the more vulnerable you are to personal lawsuits arising from car accidents and injuries that occur on your property.

YOUR INSURANCE...

Insurance is your first line of defense against a lawsuit.

TWO REASONS: The policy will pay off if you're found liable. And the insurance company may be required to defend you—saving you costly legal fees.

Review the policies you now hold. Make sure you're covered for every future legal action you may be exposed to. **KEY POLICIES TO HAVE...**

• ***Umbrella policy.*** It supplements the coverage under your homeowner's and car insurance policies. Such a policy typically provides an additional $1 million to $10 million in coverage. The greater your personal wealth, the bigger your umbrella policy should be.

• ***D&O coverage.*** If you serve as a corporate director or officer—or as a member of the board of directors of a nonprofit organization—make sure you're covered for actions against directors and officers. Ask to see a copy of the policy before agreeing to serve in such positions.

• ***Malpractice insurance.*** If you are a doctor, lawyer or other professional who may be the object of a malpractice suit, be sure you understand the extent of your policy's coverage—the types of legal actions it will and will not cover.

CHANGE OF OWNERSHIP...

How are your assets owned? The way you hold title to property can make it less vulnerable to creditors' claims. **CONSIDER THESE CHANGES...**

• ***Transfer assets to your spouse or children.*** Assuming that transfers are made before a problem comes up, this strategy should fully protect the assets.

• ***Change title of jointly owned assets into "tenancy by the entirety."*** When real estate is held in tenancy by the entirety, the creditors of one spouse can't get at the assets of the other.

In a few states (such as Florida, Pennsylvania and Virginia), tenancy by the entirety can be used for more than just real estate. In those states, it can, for instance, be used to protect brokerage accounts.

• ***Create family limited partnerships to own securities.*** While this strategy does not fully protect the holdings, it makes it more difficult for creditors to reach them.

ALTERNATIVE: Set up a charitable remainder trust to own the securities. You can receive an income for life from the trust, with the assets then passing to the charity. Tax-wise, you obtain an immediate income tax deduction for the value of the charity's remainder interest.

For asset protection purposes, creditors may be able to reach your income interest in a charitable remainder trust—but probably only for a limited number of years (typically a judgment runs for 10 years). If this happens, you will at least have protected the remaining years of income and all of the underlying trust assets.

• ***Set up a limited liability company to own any real estate now held in your name.*** Then, if any legal action arises from the real estate, your personal assets will be protected.

BANKRUPTCY EXEMPTIONS...

Federal and state bankruptcy laws let you protect certain assets from creditors—even if your financial situation is so dire that you must file for bankruptcy.

• ***Homestead protection.*** Most states provide some protection from creditors for the equity in your home. However, under the new bankruptcy act effective on October 17, 2005, protection for a home is limited to $125,000, unless the debtor resides in a state with more generous protection, for at least 40 months prior to filing for bankruptcy.

• ***Retirement plans and IRAs.*** All assets held in qualified retirement plans and rollover IRAs are fully protected. Protection for assets in traditional and/or Roth IRAs is limited to $1 million.

• ***Annuities and life insurance.*** A certain degree of protection is offered in some states. Check your state's law.

ASSET PROTECTION TRUST...

Asset protection trusts are designed to give you unfettered access to your funds while protecting them from creditors' claims. The trusts are "self-settled," meaning you set them up with your own assets, and you remain as beneficiary.

IMPORTANT: Asset protection trusts do *not* provide you with tax savings...

• ***For income tax purposes.*** Because you continue to be the "owner" of the trust, you're taxed on trust earnings.

• ***For estate tax purposes.*** Unless the transfer is treated as a completed gift subject to gift tax, the assets must be included in your taxable estate.

• ***Domestic asset protection trusts.*** Asset protection trusts—in which you are both the grantor (or "settlor") and the beneficiary—can now be set up in Alaska, Delaware, Nevada, Rhode Island and Utah. (Colorado also allows self-settled "spendthrift trusts," but its protection for settlors is not as broad as the other states.) Unlike other self-settled trusts, state law in these jurisdictions provides protection for these trusts.

However, transfers of property to these trusts within 10 years of filing for bankruptcy are protected *only* if the transfers were not made with the intent to hinder, delay or defraud creditors.

How much protection do they offer? Residents of these states can obtain protection for assets held in these trusts. It is not clear, however, whether nonresidents can achieve the same asset protection by setting up a trust in one of these states. For example, it is unclear whether a resident of New York who sets up a Delaware asset protection trust will have his/her assets fully protected in case of court action arising in New York.

• ***Offshore asset protection trusts.*** Two dozen foreign jurisdictions cater to Americans who want to set up asset protection trusts. The most popular sites now being used—Cook Islands, Nevis, St. Lucia and St. Vincent.

CAUTION: Beware of offshore trust scams promising asset protection and no federal income taxes. At *www.irs.gov,* the IRS lists scams it has uncovered. The Financial & Tax Fraud Education Associates, Inc. Web site, *www.quatloos.com,* also lists offshore scams to avoid.

■

HOW MANY CREDIT CARDS DO YOU NEED?

Source: **Robert McKinley, CEO,** CardWeb.com, an on-line publisher of payment-card information, Frederick, MD.

The average family today has 15 credit cards. Having that many cards encourages overspending and multiplies the risk that you'll be victimized by credit card fraud.

BEST: Have two cards per adult. One card should carry the lowest rate obtainable and be used to pay off major charges over time. Use the other to make charges of convenience that you pay off in full every month. It should have no annual fee but may carry a higher interest rate, since you won't incur it. Make charges on this card also to earn bonuses, such as frequent-flier miles.

SPECIAL CASE: Obtain an additional card if you frequently make business charges—to help keep records separate.

■

BETTER BANKING

Source: **Ric Edelman, CFS,** chairman of Edelman Financial Services, Inc., Fairfax, VA, and author of *Financial Security in Troubled Times* (Harper).

If you bounce even one check, you could be denied a checking account at a new bank. Most banks will report a bounced check to their interbank service ChexSystems. And, if you later apply for a new account at another bank that uses ChexSystems, it may refuse you—for up to five years.

SELF-DEFENSE: Set up overdraft protection to ensure all checks clear.

■

HOW TO PICK A SAFE INTERNET BANK

Source: **Nancy Dunnan,** a financial adviser and author in New York City. Her latest book is *How to Invest $50–$5,000* (HarperCollins).

Some of the highest savings rates are at banks doing business on-line. Their overhead is low, which enables them to be very competitive. When checking out an on-line bank, make sure it has the FDIC logo, indicating that your money in that particular bank will be insured up to $100,000 by the Federal Deposit Insurance Corp. (FDIC).

To find the best rates on-line, visit *www.bankrate.com* and *www.banx.com.* Then, compare what you find at various banks with what money market funds, offered by the leading mutual fund companies, are paying. You can find this information at *www.imoneynet.com.*

Also read *Tips for Safe Banking Over the Internet,* available free from the FDIC. Call 877-275-3342 or log on to *www.fdic.gov/bank/individual/online/safe.html.*

■

4 

BEYOND STOCKS & BONDS: WHERE INSIDERS ARE INVESTING

WHAT TO BUY INSTEAD OF US STOCKS

Source: **Ben Inker, CFA,** director of asset allocation at Grantham, Mayo, Van Otterloo & Co., an investment management firm with over $25 billion in assets, 40 Rowes Wharf, Boston 02110.

Investors who wish to move away from US stocks and can tolerate moderate risk should choose mutual funds that are divided among these attractive asset classes...

• ***28% Treasury Inflation-Protected Securities (TIPS),*** which you can purchase directly from the US Treasury (800-722-2678 or *www.publicdebt.treas.gov*). These bonds preserve capital while earning a return that is guaranteed to outpace inflation. They pay a fixed yield. In addition, principal increases in value every year along with rises in the Consumer Price Index. I expect total returns on TIPS to outpace those of stocks for the next four years.

CAUTION: Hold TIPS in tax-deferred retirement accounts, since they can generate substantial annual tax bills otherwise. Investors with taxable accounts should think about tax-free municipal bonds as alternatives. The value of munis does not rise with inflation, but their higher yields will offset the effects of inflation.

• ***20% international small-cap value stocks or funds.*** The best bets are companies in Japan and developed markets in Europe —dull businesses that have been around for generations. Many are niche manufacturers or retailers. With European investors shunning small stocks, many sell for single-digit P/Es.

Foreign stocks and bonds will get an extra boost from any future declines in the dollar.

• ***20% long-short funds.*** These funds buy stocks of undervalued companies (long positions) and then take short positions in overvalued stocks. Short sellers borrow a stock and then sell it, betting that the price will decline so they can buy it back at a lower price. They profit on the price difference.

EXAMPLE: From 1997 through 2001, these so-called market-neutral securities hedge funds returned 18.1% annually, while the S&P 500 Index returned 10.7%. And, from 1988 to 2004, they returned 17.7% annually, while the S&P returned 12.4%.*

Because they are designed to succeed in both up and down markets, these funds should prove to be ideal for the uncertain road ahead.

• ***14% emerging-market bonds.*** Many bonds issued by governments of emerging-market countries yield more than 12%. Some of these countries will default. But if you invest through diversified mutual funds, the steep yields should more than compensate for any losses.

• ***10% real estate investment trusts (REITs) or REIT funds.*** These companies own portfolios of mainly commercial properties, from office buildings to shopping malls.

Because they must pay out 90% of their income as dividends, REITs deliver generous yields. Values of commercial properties look stable because there is no overbuilding. Since the owners can raise rents over time, profits and dividends of REITs should grow at least as fast as inflation, ensuring healthy returns from these investments.

• ***8% emerging-markets stocks or funds.*** The stocks from Latin America and Asia are risky, but the overall P/E for those regions is roughly the historical average, so there is little downside.

*Statistics from Van Hedge Fund Advisors.

Some companies' stocks sell for less than the value of their assets. The best way for individuals to invest is through diversified emerging-market stock funds.

■

HOW TO ESCAPE INVESTMENT TRAPS

Source: **Arthur Levitt,** the former chairman of the Securities and Exchange Commission (1993–2001). He was previously chairman of the American Stock Exchange and cofounder and president of a major Wall Street firm, now part of Citigroup. Mr. Levitt is senior adviser at The Carlyle Group, a private equity investing firm in Greenwich, CT. He is author of *Take on the Street: What Wall Street and Corporate America Don't Want You to Know* (Pantheon).

Investing in stocks still makes sense, even during turbulent times, but you must protect yourself from the system's flaws.

Here's a former SEC chairman's advice on how to fight back...

BREAK WITH BROKERS...

Brokers are supposed to be the financial whizzes who make money for you.

REALITY: They are just salespeople working on commission. Whether you win or lose, they make money on each trade.

STRATEGY: Fire your broker. The best brokers are good people stuck in a bad system.

IF YOU HAVE LESS THAN $50,000 TO INVEST: Stick to low-cost index funds. Index funds allow your portfolio to grow with the market without paying broker commissions to buy individual stocks. Buying several types of indexes provides diversification.

Buy a mutual fund that follows either the Wilshire 5000 Index, which includes virtually all US stocks, or the S&P 500 Index, which tracks the largest US companies.

Then expand your portfolio to encompass mutual funds that track indexes of small, medium and large companies or indexes that track growth and value stocks. Put a small amount into an international fund.

IF YOU HAVE MORE THAN $50,000 TO INVEST: Retain a professional investment adviser to manage your money. Most will charge about 1% of total assets per year. The more your assets grow, the more he/she earns—giving him a powerful incentive to choose the best investments.

WHERE TO LOOK: Check out the National Association of Personal Financial Advisors at *www.napfa.org*. Certified financial planners who are members must submit their work for peer review and can operate only on a fee-for-services basis.

Match your investment strategy—based on personal goals and risk tolerance—with a like-minded adviser. Create a partnership with someone who will answer basic questions without being patronizing. I can't overstate the importance of good chemistry.

IMPORTANT: Stay in close contact with your adviser. During my Wall Street days, a few of my clients consistently outperformed the others. They were the ones who always asked why I bought this bond or failed to buy that stock.

ANALYSIS OVER ANALYSTS...

Securities analysts are supposed to be impartial researchers who recommend only the most promising stocks.

REALITY: Since fixed brokerage commissions were abolished in 1975, Wall Street firms have relied on investment banking as a major source of revenue. Acting as the intermediary between companies seeking capital and investors can create conflicts of interest. The best way for a firm to get a company's investment banking business is to give consistently positive analyst reports on that company.

STRATEGY: Consult with your financial adviser, but also do your own investment research. Relying entirely on an adviser will not get you the best results.

Plenty of high-quality independent investment research is available. Most offer free or low-cost trial subscriptions. **THESE ARE GOOD SOURCES...**

• ***Dick Davis Digest.*** The best recommendations picked from hundreds of other financial newsletters. 24 issues. $145/yr. 800-654-1514, *www.dickdavis.com*.

• ***Dow Theory Forecasts.*** Has offered good advice in both bull and bear markets since 1946. Weekly. $22.95/mo. 800-233-5922, *www.dowtheory.com*.

• ***Standard & Poor's Outlook.*** Ranks overall investment suitability of more than 1,000 companies. Weekly. $298/yr., including free information on-line. 800-852-1641.

WEB-ONLY SERVICE: *www.spoutlookonline.com.* $234/yr.

• ***Value Line Investment Survey.*** Gives three- to five-year outlooks on 1,700 stocks. Weekly. $598/yr. Also available at most libraries. 800-634-3583, *www.valueline.com.*

• ***Zacks Investment Research.*** Web site provides market news, the best analysts' reports and more. Most content is free. *www.zacks.com.*

DON'T TRUST COMPANY INFORMATION...

Companies "manage" their earnings to keep their stock high. While recent reforms will reduce this problem, they will not eliminate it.

STRATEGY: Go beyond what the companies themselves tell you about their stocks. Read the 10-K reports that they file annually with the SEC. Organizations must disclose everything that might affect future performance, such as lawsuits, shrinking market share or patent expiration.

At *www.sec.gov/edgar.shtml,* click on "Search for Company Filings" to see 10-K reports. You may not be able to analyze everything, but there are some red flags. **LOOK OUT FOR...**

• ***Pro forma earnings,*** a restatement of earnings that excludes specific factors. If the report touts pro forma earnings, assume that there is something the company doesn't want you to see. In the 1990s, companies started using pro forma earnings to exclude expenses that might reduce earnings.

EXAMPLES: Depreciation, amortization and interest are routine expenses that should not be excluded.

• ***Big write-offs.*** There is nothing wrong with writing off one-time costs, such as closing a facility or selling an unprofitable unit. In the 1990s, however, companies began writing off everyday operating expenses. US companies took $165 billion in write-offs in 2001, more than the previous five years combined.

Examine a big write-off—was it for something unusual or a routine expense that would have lowered earnings?

EXAMPLE: Goodwill, the premium a company pays over the book value of a firm it is buying, is an ordinary expense.

• ***Stock options.*** Accounting for executive stock options is a contentious issue. If they are listed as expenses in profit-and-loss statements, fine. If they appear only in footnotes to company reports, avoid those companies.

■

MAKING UP FOR BIG MARKET LOSSES

Source: **Jonathan Clements,** financial columnist for *The Wall Street Journal* and author of *25 Myths You've Got to Avoid If You Want to Manage Your Money Right: The New Rules of Financial Success* (Simon & Schuster).

Those whose retirement nest eggs have lost ground might want to consider the following three ways to get themselves back on track...

• ***Invest fresh savings.*** If you're able, bolster your retirement portfolio by adding in more shares, purchased at lower prices. Also, rebalance within your stock portfolio to maintain your target percentages in each category. This will force you to sell what has appreciated and to take advantage of lower share prices in other sectors.

• ***Get help from dividends.*** When share prices are falling, take advantage by reinvesting all of your dividends.

• ***Try value averaging.*** This is a combination of dollar cost averaging (investing the same amount regularly every month) and rebalancing. It was developed by Michael Edleson, former Harvard Business School professor.

HOW IT WORKS: You try to make your portfolio grow by a specified amount each month. Instead of investing a flat $100 every month, for example, if the first $100 falls to, say, $95 during the month, you would make a contribution of $105 the second month.

In months where portfolio growth was more than $100, you might not invest the next month, or you might even sell some shares. Historically, this strategy has produced even better results than dollar cost averaging.

■

FINANCIAL MAKEOVERS

Source: **Ross Levin, CFP,** founding principal and president of Accredited Investors, Inc., a financial planning firm, Edina, MN. He is author of *The Wealth Management Index* (McGraw-Hill) and has served as chairman of the International Association for Financial Planning.

Your elderly parents are struggling financially...you're house-rich but cash-poor...you want to retire early but are not sure you can afford to.

Over and over again, clients ask financial planner Ross Levin for solutions to tricky money problems such as these. **HIS ADVICE CAN HELP YOU, TOO...**

TOO MUCH HOUSE...

TYPICAL SCENARIO: A retired 68-year-old woman came to me with a $600,000 portfolio and a house in Minneapolis worth $500,000. Her children were pressuring her to downsize to a condo in Florida. She wasn't sure if it was a smart move personally or financially.

My advice to her...

• ***Figure out whether you can support yourself in retirement without selling your home.*** Many retirees count their home's value in their net worth, but they may not reap the full value if they need to sell it quickly.

The woman determined that she had an adequate income—$60,000 per year. I advised her not to move.

HELPFUL: T. Rowe Price's Web site (*www3.troweprice.com/ric/RIC*) has a retirement income calculator, or call 800-831-1432 for information.

• ***If you decide to stay put,*** upgrade your home to accommodate your needs as you age.

EXAMPLES: Install better lighting in the kitchen and levers on doors instead of knobs...put railings in the bathroom...add antiscald valves to faucets.

• ***Consider downsizing if it makes financial sense.*** Your home has risen steadily in value...you would profit by moving to a smaller residence or a town with a lower cost of living...you need the money to boost your retirement savings.

HELPFUL: To find cost of living comparisons, go to author Bert Sperling's Web site, *www.bestplaces.net.*

TAPPING SOCIAL SECURITY...

TYPICAL SCENARIO: An unmarried salesman, age 55, was making $75,000 a year. He wanted to retire early and work part-time for $25,000 a year for about 10 years. Income from his investments would provide another $25,000. Before making a decision, he wanted to know how much he could expect in Social Security payments and when to start taking payments.

My advice to him...

• ***Evaluate your health.*** The longer you expect to live, the more it pays to delay retirement. Do you have serious health issues, such as heart disease? Did your parents and grandparents live beyond normal life expectancy?

• ***Factor in the income effect.*** If you take Social Security at the earliest age of 62 instead of full retirement age (age 66 for those born in between 1943–1954), you get 20% to 30% less per month. For my client, that's $365 less a month for life.

Working a few extra years full-time also will give your nest egg more time to grow. In contrast, if you were to work part-time while collecting Social Security from age 62 to full retirement age, you would lose $1 in benefits for each $2 you earn over a certain amount ($12,000 in 2005).

UPSHOT: My client was in good health and expected to live into his mid-80s, as his father did. He had sufficient assets and income to maintain his standard of living for 10 years. He decided to take Social Security at full retirement age, about $1,700 a month.

To find out how much you will receive based on when you draw your benefits, fill out Form SSA-7004, *Request for Social Security Statement,* from the Social Security Administration. 800-772-1213, *www.socialsecurity.gov.*

FINDING CASH FAST FOR COLLEGE...

TYPICAL SCENARIO: A couple in their 50s had saved for their son's education since he was born. They failed to move into conservative investments before the bear market took hold in 2000. Even after a recent rally, their $100,000 account was down to $50,000. Their son was accepted to an Ivy League school with tuition of more than $30,000 a year. The parents did not qualify for financial aid. They did not want their son to attend a community college for the first year or two (average tuition—less than $2,000 each year) because there was no guarantee that he could later transfer to an Ivy League school. They considered borrowing from their 401(k)s.

My advice to them...

• ***Keep the $50,000 invested*** to cover tuition in years three and four. Invest the $50,000 of college savings in a balanced mutual fund that includes bonds and large-cap, small-cap and international stocks. Vanguard Life-Strategy funds are available in a variety of allocations, depending on your stage of life. 877-662-7447, *www.vanguard.com.*

• ***To cover the first two years,*** don't take loans from your 401(k) plans. **INSTEAD, CONSIDER A...**

• Parent loan for undergraduate students (PLUS). These loans require no collateral. Their interest is adjusted annually by the Department of Education. Eligibility is based on credit history, not on financial need. Payments are deferred until 60 days after the loan is dispersed.

FOR MORE INFORMATION: 800-413-7737, *www.parentplusloan.com.*

• ***Arrange to spread tuition payments over 12 months*** without interest, rather than handing over a lump sum each semester. Your money can earn interest in the meantime.

SHORTCUT: Academic Management Services (AMS) works with more than 1,500 colleges and universities to arrange payment plans for students.

COST: About $50 per year to enroll. You can authorize a direct payment every month from your checking account. 800-635-0120 or log on to *www.tuitionpay.com.*

ELDERLY PARENTS FACING A CASH CRUNCH...

TYPICAL SCENARIO: A 56-year-old businessman contacted me about his retired parents. Their income had been cut by 45% due to losses from the bear market and record-low interest rates. He didn't have a lot of spare cash, but he wanted to help them. He also worried that they were too proud to accept his help.

My advice to him...

• ***Offer to pay for specific expenses*** instead of offering them a general handout.

EXAMPLES: Part of their electric bill...drugs that aren't covered by insurance.

To help them save face, say, "You made a lot of sacrifices for me, and now it's my turn to do something for you."

IMPORTANT: Give no more than $11,000 annually to each parent to avoid gift tax. (Direct payments of any amount to a doctor or hospital are not subject to gift tax.)

• ***Encourage your parents to consider a reverse mortgage if they don't plan to move.*** A typical reverse mortgage boosts income by 13% to 19%. The home owner receives the money tax free in either a lump sum or installments for the rest of his/her life. The loan becomes payable only after the borrower dies or sells the house.

NOTE: While fees are high, they often are included in the loan amount, so there's little up-front cost.

FOR MORE INFORMATION: The National Reverse Mortgage Lenders Association. 202-939-1760, *www.reversemortgage.org.*

■

A GIANT TAX BREAK FOR HOME OWNERS

Source: **Janice M. Johnson, CPA, JD,** A.B. Watley Group, 90 Park Ave., New York City 10016.

The gain on the sale of a home is tax free up to $250,000 ($500,000 on a joint return) when you have used the home as your main residence for at least two of the prior five years. You can make such a tax-free sale once every two years.

If you own other residences (such as vacation or investment properties) in addition to your principal residence, you can move into them for two years at a time to take the tax-free gain on them, too, when selling them.

■

5 

THE NEW ANSWERS TO CANCER

THE ULTIMATE DISEASE-FIGHTING DIET

Source: **Bradley J. Willcox, MD,** physician-scientist, Pacific Health Research Institute, and clinical assistant professor of geriatrics, University of Hawaii, both in Honolulu. He is coauthor of *The Okinawa Diet Plan: Get Leaner, Live Longer, and Never Feel Hungry* (Clarkson Potter).

For many years, US government scientists have been urging Americans to consume at least *five* daily servings of fruits and vegetables. But that's not nearly enough, according to recent research.

For maximum longevity, look to the fruit- and vegetable-rich diet of the world's longest-lived people—the men and women living in Okinawa, Japan.

During 25 years of study, researchers have found that Okinawans have healthier arteries...lower risk for hormone-dependent malignancies, such as breast and prostate cancer ...stronger bones...sharper minds...lean, fit bodies...and excellent emotional health.

Okinawans eat mainly high-carbohydrate, low-calorie, plant-based foods—the same diet deemed optimal for long-term health by more than 2,000 scientific studies.

At first glance, the Okinawa diet seems like a lot of food to eat each day. The trick is to remember that a daily serving, as defined by the United States Department of Agriculture (USDA), is quite small.

EXAMPLE: For raw, leafy vegetables, a serving is one cup. For whole grains, a serving is one-half cup of cooked cereal, one slice of bread or half a bagel.

If you adhere to the Okinawa program, in which plant-based foods comprise two-thirds of the diet, you will exceed the USDA dietary recommendations.

Here is how scientists have recently adapted the Okinawa diet for Americans...

• ***Eat until you are 80% full.*** Okinawans say, *hara hachi bu,* "Eat until you are eight parts full (out of 10)."

Restricting calories is a proven way to prolong life and vitality. Fewer calories will mean fewer free radicals, which are the molecules responsible for the biochemical damage that causes aging.

This doesn't mean Okinawans eat less. In fact, they eat more food by weight than North Americans. But they eat small amounts of fat and sugar, which are calorie-dense.

To eliminate excess calories...

- Flavor meals with spices instead of fat.
- When cooking, spray the oil instead of pouring—two seconds of spraying equals one-half teaspoon of oil.
- Use heart-healthy canola oil.
- Start your lunch with a chunky, low-fat soup. If you do, you'll eat 20% fewer calories.
- When dining out, order lean fish instead of steak...ask for fatty sauces and dressings to be served on the side...and try to share desserts.

• ***Eat nine to 17 servings of vegetables and fruits daily.*** A diet rich in fruits and vegetables decreases your risk for heart disease, cancer, stroke, high blood pressure and obesity.

Fruits and vegetables are full of healthful nutrients—but low in calories. They also contain antioxidants, which help to protect you against free radicals.

To increase your consumption of fruits and vegetables...

• At breakfast, eat a fruit salad with cantaloupe, strawberries, blueberries and apples.

• At lunch, include vegetables like tomato, broccoli and celery in a salad.

• At dinner, make a vegetable soup with onions, zucchini and carrots.

• ***Eat seven to 13 servings of whole-grain foods daily.*** Whole grains are rich in nutrients, antioxidants and fiber. These constituents decrease your risk for heart disease, stroke, diabetes and cancer.

Many different types of whole grains—from amaranth, barley and bulgur to rice, triticale (a high-protein hybrid of wheat and rye) and wheat—are in cereals, breads and pastas.

FOR MAXIMUM BENEFIT: Choose breakfast cereals that contain at least seven grams of fiber per serving.

• ***Eat two to four servings of calcium foods daily.*** Calcium fights osteoporosis and may help to prevent colon cancer, high blood pressure and premenstrual syndrome. Good plant sources of calcium include green, leafy vegetables...calcium-fortified soy products, like tofu and soy milk...and calcium-fortified orange juice.

IMPORTANT: Low-fat dairy products may not be the best source of calcium. The protein in dairy products may leach the calcium from your bones.

• ***Eat two to four servings of flavonoid-rich foods daily.*** Blood levels of flavonoids—beneficial compounds found in all plants—are up to 50 times higher in the Japanese than in white Americans, according to a recent study. A high-flavonoid diet may help prevent heart disease as well as breast, prostate and colon cancers.

Isoflavone-rich soy products contain flavonoid levels that are up to 1,000 times greater than those found in other foods.

Flaxseed contains high levels of lignans, which are similar compounds. And, beans are another good source, followed by tea, onions and apples.

To increase your intake of flavonoids and lignans...

• Eat soy products twice a day. Choices include tofu, miso (a salty paste often used as a flavoring), soy milk, soy nuts and soy burgers.

• Take one tablespoon of flaxseed oil daily, or use it instead of butter or as a salad dressing.

• Drink three cups of tea daily.

• Emphasize flavonoid-rich fruits and vegetables, such as broccoli, kale, celery, onions, snow peas, turnip greens, apples, strawberries, grapes and apricots.

• ***Eat one to three servings of omega-3 foods every day.*** Most Americans do not consume enough of the omega-3 fatty acids. These dietary constituents protect your brain, arteries and immune system.

To boost your intake of omega-3 foods...

• Eat fatty fish (salmon, tuna and mackerel) three times a week.

• Add flaxseed to your diet. Mix it into pancake or muffin batter or other baked goods.

• ***Avoid red meat.*** It may increase your risk for colon and prostate cancer. Do not eat red meat more than three times a week—and choose lean cuts.

• ***Drink fresh water.*** You need adequate hydration. But forget about the eight-glasses-a-day rule.

BETTER: Drink enough so that your urine is clear to straw-colored, whether that's four or 12 glasses a day.

■

CANCER FIGHTER ON A SANDWICH

Source: **Paul Talalay, MD,** professor of pharmacology at Johns Hopkins University, Brassica Chemoprotection Laboratory, 725 N. Wolfe St., Baltimore 21205.

Broccoli sprouts are rich in a compound that provides significant protection against breast and colon cancers. Sprouts grown from certain broccoli seeds contain up to 50 times more of this compound—*sulforaphane glucosinolate* (SGS)—than mature broccoli.

CAUTION: SGS amounts in broccoli sprouts vary widely.

BroccoSprouts, a brand developed at Johns Hopkins University, is guaranteed to have 20 times the SGS of mature broccoli on an ounce-for-ounce basis. *www.broccosprouts.com.*

■

NEW SKIN CANCER WEAPON

Source: **Perry Robins, MD,** president, Skin Cancer Foundation, 245 Fifth Ave., Suite 1403, New York City 10016, *www.skincancer.org.*

Chemoprevention uses oral and topical therapies to treat the skin after it has been damaged by sun, but before the damage has ended in cancer. Treatments include vitamin A, antioxidants, aspirin and other nonsteroidal anti-inflammatory drugs, and enzymes.

CAUTION: Chemoprevention is only one part of cancer prevention. Sun avoidance, use of sunscreen and appropriate clothing, and skin examination all remain important.

■

IMPROVE YOUR HEALTH WITH THE CRON DIET

Source: The late **Roy Walford, MD,** former professor of pathology at the University of California at Los Angeles School of Medicine. Dr. Walford was recognized internationally as one of the top experts in the field of gerontology. He published more than 350 scientific articles and six books, including *Beyond the 120-Year Diet* (Four Walls Eight Windows).

In September 1991, Roy Walford, MD, joined seven other scientists as the crew physician for a two-year experiment within an enclosed, earthlike environment in the Arizona desert known as Biosphere 2.

THE MISSION: To develop technology in order to create self-sustained bases on the moon and Mars.

As part of the experiment, Dr. Walford put the crew on what he dubbed the CRON diet, for *Calorie Restriction with Optimal Nutrition*. Based on this research, Dr. Walford hypothesized that calorie restriction could be used to significantly increase longevity.

After six months, Biosphere 2 crew members experienced dramatic decreases in their blood pressure, insulin levels, cholesterol, triglycerides, white blood cell counts and other "biomarkers" of health.

Recent scientific evidence supports Dr. Walford's belief that life span can be dramatically lengthened, beyond the average US life span of 77 years, simply through diet.

The scientific community has recently begun to support the theory that human life span can be significantly extended.

The evidence in this area has advanced markedly during the past 10 years. For example, genetic manipulation of yeast, worms, flies and even mice has recently extended life spans.

Even though genetic manipulation does not involve calorie restriction, it operates in much the same manner. For example, researchers at the University of Wisconsin recently discovered that 84% of the mice genes that display age-related alterations were either completely or partially counteracted by a calorie-restricted diet.

Whichever theory of aging one looks at, the experimental results produced by the CRON diet appear to slow all the primary aging factors.

And the CRON diet not only extends life span but also favorably affects the risk factors for heart disease, stroke, cancer, diabetes and autoimmune disorders.

In one recent experiment with mice that were genetically programmed to get breast cancer, the malignancy rates were reduced from an expected 55% to 5% or less when a calorie-restricted diet was administered. This result is typical of other rodent studies using the CRON diet.

What's more, monkeys that eat a calorie-restricted diet are healthier and live longer than monkeys not on this type of diet, according to studies being conducted at the National Institute on Aging, the University of Maryland and the University of Wisconsin.

FOODS ON THE CRON DIET...

For this diet to work properly, every calorie must be nutrient packed. For example, the basic salad, which is a staple of all lunch and dinner meals, contains an assortment of highly nutritious ingredients. These include romaine lettuce, chopped spinach, yellow squash, red bell pepper, raw sweet potato, raw broccoli or broccoli sprouts, red cabbage, red or yellow onions, long-grain brown rice with chestnuts, cooked beans and fresh salsa, dressed to taste with balsamic vinegar, extra-virgin olive oil and seasonings.

The CRON diet also includes whole grains, fruit and low-fat or skim milk. If you like meat, add three and a half ounces of lean red meat just once a week. Ostrich, emu and bison all have a low saturated fat content. Fish and poultry, such as chicken and turkey, can be eaten twice a week.

STARTING THE CRON DIET...

You have to be patient to try this eating plan. First, change to a healthful, nutrient-dense diet, such as the one described, for a few months without trying to reduce calories. Find a physician who is knowledgeable about life extension to monitor your health. To do so, call your local medical society and ask for a list of practitioners who are attending physicians at a local hospital and who specialize in aging and life extension. Also, contact the American Geriatrics Society, 800-563-4916, *www.healthinaging.org.*

The physician should measure your blood pressure, cholesterol, triglycerides, blood sugar, white blood cell count and thyroid status, including your T3 hormone levels, every six months. All of these readings should improve rapidly if you are doing the diet correctly.

Finally, start cutting your calories—to 2,000 a day if you are an average-sized man or to 1,800 a day if you are an average-sized woman. Your goal is to achieve a weight that is 10% to 25% below your "set point." That's your characteristic weight when you don't overeat or undereat.

You can find a group of people who follow the diet at *www.calorierestriction.org.*

HEALTH RISKS OF THE CRON DIET...

The main risk is going too far, too fast. Studies show the body needs time to healthfully adapt to any major metabolic change. If you're feeling physically or mentally fatigued, for example, you're going too fast. You should feel better on this diet. That's why it's advisable to be monitored by a doctor for at least the first year.

■

SCHOOL BUS WARNING

Source: **Gina Solomon, MD, MPH,** a senior scientist at the Natural Resources Defense Council, San Francisco.

Toxic diesel fumes can increase cancer risk and exacerbate asthma and other breathing problems. In a recent study, exhaust levels inside diesel buses were 23 to 46 times *higher* than levels considered a significant cancer risk.

WORST PLACE: Back of a bus more than 10 years old (age is indicated on a plaque above the inside windshield).

Ask the driver to keep windows open...and encourage your child to sit toward the front.

■

GOOD SLEEP HELPS FIGHT CANCER

Source: **Sandra Sephton, PhD,** assistant scientist, James Graham Brown Cancer Center, University of Louisville School of Medicine, KY.

Sleep influences the stress hormone cortisol, which may play a role in cancer. Disruption of normal sleep/wake rhythms, such as shift work, seems to reduce the body's defenses against developing cancer.

SELF-DEFENSE: Keep to a regular sleep schedule as much as possible.

■

6 

AMAZING NEW PAIN CURES YOUR DOCTOR DIDN'T KNOW ABOUT

ANSWER FOR CHRONIC PAIN

Source: **Dharma Singh Khalsa, MD,** president and medical director of the Alzheimer's Prevention Foundation in Tucson, AZ, and author of *The Pain Cure* (Warner Books). He is board-certified in anesthesiology, pain management and antiaging medicine.

Twenty-five million Americans are bedeviled by some form of chronic pain—sciatica, migraine, arthritis, muscle pain, etc. There are effective ways to curb chronic pain, but these aren't the ways typically recommended by mainstream physicians.

Here are eight pain-relieving strategies that really work…

• ***Eat more fish and poultry.*** Doctors often prescribe *fluoxetine* (Prozac) for chronic pain. This prescription antidepressant helps curb pain by boosting levels of the neurotransmitter *serotonin* in the brain. Serotonin blocks synthesis of *substance P,* one of the main chemical messengers involved in chronic pain.

But many people can keep serotonin levels high simply by eating foods rich in *tryptophan,* an amino acid that the body converts into serotonin.

Two excellent sources of tryptophan are poultry and fish. If you have chronic pain, try eating three ounces of either one five days a week. In addition to blocking substance P, serotonin helps make people less aware of pain by improving mood and regulating disturbed sleep cycles.

• ***Eat a banana every day.*** Most chronic pain stems from arthritis, muscle pain or another inflammatory condition, which invariably goes hand in hand with muscle spasms. These muscle spasms contribute to chronic pain.

Eat one banana a day—along with a bit of the lining of the peel that you've scraped off with a spoon. Doing so will supply you with lots of magnesium and potassium. Both minerals help control spasms.

• ***Get regular exercise.*** Exercise triggers the synthesis of natural painkillers known as *endorphins.*

Of course, if you're experiencing severe pain, you probably don't feel like doing vigorous exercise. That's fine. Endorphin synthesis can be triggered by any form of activity that pushes the body a bit harder than it's accustomed to.

If you've been sedentary for a long time, something as simple as rotating your arms for a few seconds can work. So can sitting in a chair and raising your legs a few times.

• ***Take steps to control psychological stress.*** Stress plays a central role in chronic pain. Meditation and other relaxation techniques reduce muscle spasms, limit the release of pain-causing stress hormones and improve breathing. Each of these helps reduce pain intensity.

One recent study found that pain sufferers who meditated for 10 to 20 minutes a day visited a pain clinic 36% less often than did their nonmeditating peers.

WHAT TO DO: Carve out at least 15 minutes of quiet time each day. If you aren't comfortable meditating, use the time to pray...visualize a tranquil scene...or sit quietly.

• ***Avoid harmful fats.*** Red meat and cooking oil stimulate production of *arachidonic acid,* a compound that the body converts into hormone-like substances that trigger inflammation. These substances are known as *prostaglandins.*

Chronic pain sufferers should avoid red meat entirely...and use cooking oil sparingly.

• ***Take a vitamin B-complex supplement.*** Chronic pain is often accompanied by fatigue. When you feel more energetic, your pain tends to be more manageable. Ask your doctor about taking a daily supplement that contains at least 50 milligrams (mg) of B-complex vitamins.

Vitamin B helps increase energy levels by facilitating the production of *ATP,* the high-energy compound found in mitochondria, the "power plants" inside cells.

• ***Try acupuncture.*** There's now solid evidence that acupuncture can be more effective than drug therapy for relieving many types of chronic pain.

Acupuncture that is done by a physician seems to be especially effective. So-called medical acupuncture often involves the application of electrical current to needles inserted into one's skin. This variation is called electroacupuncture.

For referral to an acupuncturist, contact the American Academy of Medical Acupuncture at *www.medicalacupuncture.org.*

• ***See a chiropractor or osteopath.*** Most physicians rely upon drug therapy and surgery for controlling pain. Chiropractors and osteopaths incorporate physical manipulation into their treatments. For back pain especially, manipulation frequently works better than drugs or surgery.

■

NO MORE NECK PAIN

Source: **Robert A. Lavin, MD,** assistant professor of neurology and director, chronic pain management service, Baltimore Veterans Administration Medical Health Care System. His study was published in the *Archives of Physical Medicine and Rehabilitation.*

To ease neck pain, sleep on a water pillow. Volunteers who slept on pillows with adjustable water-filled pouches for two weeks indicated better sleep and less pain when they awoke than those who slept on down-filled, foam or roll pillows. Water pillows are available from selected home/health care stores.

COST: About $50.

■

NEW HELP FOR CHRONIC BACK PAIN

Source: **Yung Chen, MD,** interventional spine pain specialist, physical medicine and rehabilitation, Spinal Diagnostics and Treatment Center, Dale City, CA.

Chronic back pain can be eased in less than 30 minutes via an outpatient procedure used for people with mildly herniated disks and sciatica. *Nucleoplasty* is faster and safer than other intradiscal procedures. This involves inserting a needle into the disk and releasing radio-frequency energy that heats the area, vaporizing tissue inside the disk. Performed under a local anesthetic, nucleoplasty provides, on average, a 70% reduction in pain.

■

ALL ABOUT LEG CRAMPS

Source: **Norman Marcus, MD,** president, Norman Marcus Pain Institute, New York City. He is also the author of *Freedom from Pain* (Fireside).

If you've been experiencing leg cramps but have neglected to do something about them, you may be placing your life in jeopardy.

REASON: While two of the three main types of leg cramps are benign, a walking-related cramp known as *intermittent claudication* is a sign of atherosclerosis.

- ***Symptoms.*** If walking gives you a cramp in one of your calves, see your doctor right away. Unlike other types of leg cramps, intermittent claudication is caused by reduced blood flow in one of the legs. In most instances, this reduction in blood flow is caused by the buildup of fatty deposits in the leg arteries (atherosclerosis).

DANGER: People who have fatty deposits in their leg arteries often have similar deposits in their coronary arteries. In fact, if someone has claudication, there is a 50% chance that he/she also has heart disease.

Claudication causes bad cramps in one leg after walking even a short distance. Typically, the cramp disappears after a minute or two of rest...and recurs when you resume walking.

OTHER SYMPTOMS: Having one foot that has thicker toenails, is bluish in color, has less hair or is colder than the other foot.

Treatment for intermittent claudication is similar to that for coronary artery disease. In most cases, patients are urged to take long walks or get other regular aerobic exercise...quit smoking...and adopt a low-fat, low-cholesterol diet.

Some cases of intermittent claudication require leg surgery to clear away the blockages. Doctors are able to push aside the fatty deposits by snaking a balloon-tipped catheter through the skin and into the clogged artery. This procedure is called *balloon angioplasty*.

For severe cases, bypass surgery may be required. In this procedure, the surgeon creates a "detour" around the blocked arteries by grafting a blood vessel from a large artery in the groin to an artery behind the knee.

In some cases, individuals who experience walking-related leg cramps are suffering not from claudication but from a condition called *pseudoclaudication*.

This comparatively benign condition is caused by abnormal growth of bone tissue in the spine. As the bone grows, the bony sheath encasing the lower spinal nerves narrows. That compresses the nerves, causing them to register pain.

How can you tell pseudoclaudication from true claudication? Pain from claudication goes away within two minutes when you stop walking. Pain from pseudoclaudication persists for five to 10 minutes.

If pseudoclaudication is accompanied by leg weakness and loss of sensation, surgery may be needed. Injections of cortisone and local anesthetic into the spinal cord region may help decrease the pain.

Other more benign types of leg cramps...

• ***Nighttime leg cramps*** typically involve a spasm in the calf muscle—and are often strong enough to wake you up. To stop the pain, gently massage the knot while alternately flexing and extending your toes.

ALSO HELPFUL: Ask your doctor about taking the prescription medication *quinine sulfate* and about taking a supplement that contains 500 to 1,000 milligrams (mg) of calcium... 1,000 mg of magnesium...as well as 400 international units (IU) of vitamin D.

The minerals are critical to proper muscle contraction. Vitamin D assures proper absorption of the minerals.

• ***Post-exercise leg cramps*** are typically caused by electrolyte imbalances brought on by heavy perspiration. These imbalances cause muscle and nerve cells to malfunction.

HELPFUL: Rest...drink water or a sports drink like Gatorade before and during exercise...and massage after exercise.

■

FATTY ACIDS FIGHT PAINFUL DISEASES OF THE IMMUNE SYSTEM

Source: **Andrew L. Stoll, MD,** director of the psychopharmacology research laboratory at McLean Hospital, and assistant professor of psychiatry at Harvard Medical School, both in Boston. He is the author of *The Omega-3 Connection* (Simon & Schuster).

In Japan and other nations where fish is a dietary staple, many disease rates are significantly lower than in Western countries.

Omega-3 fatty acids—lipid compounds that are a major constituent of fish oil—receive much of the credit.

Many people now take omega-3 supplements to reduce their risk for heart disease, rheumatoid arthritis, obesity and diabetes. But do omega-3s really deliver all these salutary effects? And what other diseases can they help?

Distinguished researcher Andrew L. Stoll, MD, provides an explanation of the facts...

Why are omega-3 fatty acids important?

Essential fatty acids are dietary constituents that promote good health.

In addition to omega-3, there's another essential fatty acid known as omega-6. For optimum health, we need to consume roughly the same amount of omega-3s and omega-6s.

But Americans eat small quantities of fish and even less omega-3–containing plants, such as flax and the salad green purslane. Instead, our diets are loaded up with omega-6–rich oils—corn, sunflower and most oils in processed foods. We eat 10 to 20 times more omega-6s than omega-3s.

Why is this unhealthful?

Omega-3s contain *eicosapentaenoic acid* (EPA). When we consume this beneficial fat, much of it gets converted into *eicosanoids,* hormone-like substances that direct the inflammatory response and other functions within the immune system, heart and brain.

Omega-6s contain the fatty acid *arachidonic acid.* This substance also turns into eicosanoids—but with a critical difference.

Omega-6 eicosanoids are strongly inflammatory. On the other hand, omega-3 eicosanoids are only slightly inflammatory or, in some instances, anti-inflammatory.

That's why balance is so important. Without it, uncontrolled inflammatory responses can damage virtually any organ system in the body.

How do omega-3s help diseases of the immune system?

The highly inflammatory eicosanoids produced by omega-6s are great infection fighters. But when left unchecked by omega-3s, they can damage healthy tissue.

In the digestive disorder known as Crohn's disease, the gut becomes inflamed…in rheumatoid arthritis, it's the joints…in asthma, the airways are inflamed.

In a remarkable Italian study published in the *New England Journal of Medicine,* 60% of Crohn's patients who took 2.7 grams (g) of fish oil supplements daily went into remission for more than one year. No medication has proven to be more effective in treating Crohn's disease.

Studies have also indicated that omega-3s reduce the inflammation of rheumatoid arthritis and asthma.

How much omega-3 does a healthy person need?

To maintain health, 1 to 2 g a day. But it is difficult to get that much in food alone. You would have to consume, say, a large salmon steak daily.

You should certainly try to eat more omega-3–rich foods, such as salmon, tuna, mackerel and sardines…wild game meats, including buffalo and venison…flax…purslane…and walnuts. Add one to two servings a day of these foods to your diet. Still, you may not get enough omega-3s from dietary sources. To ensure adequate intake, take a daily 1 to 2 g supplement.

How do I choose the right supplement?

Look for distilled fish-oil capsules that have an omega-3 concentration of 50% or more. Quality supplements cost more, but they do enable you to take fewer and smaller pills, without the fishy aftertaste you often get with other brands.

What do you recommend for vegetarians?

Flaxseed oil is a good option for strict vegetarians or those allergic to fish. Take one-half tablespoon of this plant-based omega-3 every day. Some people will take flaxseed oil straight. Others cannot tolerate the strong taste. However, it is virtually imperceptible when used in waffle batter and other recipes.

Do omega-3 supplements have any side effects?

Omega-3s may inhibit blood clotting. If you're taking a blood thinner or high-dose aspirin, check with your physician before starting a regimen of omega-3 supplements.

Some people experience stomach upset, but this usually goes away within seven days. You'll be less likely to have this problem if you use a quality supplement...take it with food...and divide your daily intake among two or three equal doses.

By the way, it's a good idea to take vitamins C and E with omega-3s. These antioxidant vitamins scavenge the disease-causing molecules known as "free radicals." Once free radicals are eliminated, omega-3s can do their job.

I typically recommend 800 international units of vitamin E* and 1,000 milligrams of vitamin C daily. In addition to other benefits, your colds won't last as long.

■

EASY WART TREATMENT

Source: **Daniel M. Siegel, MD,** clinical associate professor of dermatology, State University of New York at Downstate.

Put duct tape over a wart, and leave it on for seven days. Then uncover the area for 12 hours. Repeat the cycle until the wart falls off. Duct tape keeps moisture in and helps break down wart tissue.

■

*Due to the possible interactions between vitamin E and various drugs and supplements as well as other safety considerations, be sure to talk to your doctor before taking vitamin E.

WORLD'S GREATEST ARTHRITIS BREAKTHROUGHS

NATURAL REMEDIES FOR ARTHRITIS PAIN

Source: **James M. Rippe, MD,** associate professor of medicine at the Tufts University School of Medicine in Boston. Dr. Rippe is the founder and director of the Rippe Lifestyle Institute in Shrewsbury, MA, and author of many books, including *The Joint Health Prescription* (Rodale).

More than half of Americans over age 40 are dealing with some type of joint complaint, from stiffness to arthritis pain. In people over age 60, joint problems account for more than 50% of all cases of disability.

In the past, doctors typically relied on painkilling drugs to treat joint ailments. But these medications do not solve the underlying problems. **HERE'S HOW TO GET LASTING RELIEF...**

EXERCISE...

A decade ago, doctors told their patients with joint pain to avoid exercise. We now know from dozens of studies that regular exercise is one of the *best* things you can do for your joints.

The perfect exercise program for healthy joints will include aerobics and stretching as well as strengthening...

• ***Aerobics.*** The safest workouts are low-impact activities, such as walking, swimming and bicycling.

Avoid running, step aerobics and jumping rope. They could cause joint injury.

• ***Stretching.*** Do head rolls, shoulder rolls and hamstring stretches.

• ***Strengthening.*** Use dumbbells or weight machines. Stretching and strengthening exercises help cushion and stabilize the joints.

TO START AN EXERCISE PROGRAM: Perform 10 minutes of aerobic exercise a day. Every week, increase that time by five minutes until you are getting 30 minutes of moderate aerobic activity every day. Do stretching exercises every morning and night. Strengthening exercises should be done every other day.

You do *not* have to do all your daily exercise at one time—as long as you accumulate 30 minutes of activity throughout the day. Gardening, housework and taking the stairs all count.

CAUTION: If you already have arthritis or another serious joint condition, such as from a prior injury, have your doctor and/or physical therapist recommend some appropriate exercises for you to try. Anyone who has been sedentary should consult a doctor before beginning an exercise program.

WEIGHT LOSS AND NUTRITION...

If you are overweight, losing even 10 pounds will reduce wear and tear on your joints. Even if you are not overweight, proper nutrition can help keep your joints healthy.

Be skeptical of any "arthritis diet" that claims to cure joint pain by promoting a single type of food or eliminating whole categories of foods. **INSTEAD, JUST FOLLOW BASIC PRINCIPLES OF GOOD NUTRITION...**

• ***Avoid unhealthy fats.*** A high-fat diet triggers inflammation—a key component of joint problems. This is especially true of saturated fat (found in many animal products, such as red meat) and omega-6 fatty acids (found in many processed foods and vegetable oils).

HELPFUL: Substitute monounsaturated fats, such as olive oil and canola oil. Favor foods rich in "good" omega-3 fatty acids, such as nuts, flaxseed and cold-water fish, including salmon and mackerel. These foods help fight inflammation.

• ***Eat more vitamin-rich foods.*** Fruits and vegetables are good sources of antioxidant vitamins. Antioxidants will neutralize the free radicals, which damage cells and contribute to joint inflammation.

Also, certain vitamins may act directly on joints. Vitamin C is involved in the production of collagen, a component of cartilage and connective tissue. Beta-carotene and vitamins D and K help in the development of strong bones.

For more information on healthy eating and nutrition, contact the American Dietetic Association, 800-877-1600, *www.eatright.org.*

SUPPLEMENTS...

Research suggests that certain supplements can help to relieve joint problems. **ASK YOUR DOCTOR WHETHER ANY OF THE FOLLOWING SUPPLEMENTS ARE RIGHT FOR YOU...***

• ***Vitamins.*** Even though food is the best way to get your vitamins, it's a good idea to take a multivitamin supplement to make sure you are getting *all* the vitamins you need. These include beta-carotene and vitamins C, D and E. Vitamin E is especially hard to get in sufficient quantities from food.

• ***Gelatin.*** It contains *glycine* and *proline,* two amino acids that are important for the rebuilding of cartilage. These amino acids are found in products made with hydrolyzed collagen protein (such as Knox NutraJoint). These products dissolve in juice without congealing—unlike cooking gelatin.

TYPICAL DAILY DOSAGE: 10 grams.

• ***Glucosamine.*** This sugar is one of the building blocks of cartilage. Increasing evidence suggests that glucosamine helps to relieve arthritis pain and stiffness—without major side effects.

TYPICAL DAILY DOSAGE: 1,500 milligrams (mg).

• ***Chondroitin.*** Naturally present in cartilage, chondroitin is believed to guard against destructive enzymes.

TYPICAL DAILY DOSAGE: 1,200 mg. A number of supplements combine glucosamine and chondroitin.

■

*Supplements can interact with each other and with drugs, so tell all your doctors everything you are taking.

WATER HELPS FIGHT OSTEOARTHRITIS

Source: **Ronald Lawrence, MD, PhD,** a founding member of the International Association for the Study of Pain, Seattle, and coauthor of *Preventing Arthritis* (Putnam).

Osteoarthritis pain may be a symptom of dehydration in the joint. Increasing water intake often improves the condition after about four weeks—the time needed to rehydrate the body. Drink half your body weight in ounces.

EXAMPLE: If you weigh 160 pounds, drink 80 ounces—10 eight-ounce glasses—daily. Drink more during the summer, when humidity is high, or when exercising.

■

WINE MAY PROTECT AGAINST ARTHRITIS

Source: **Alberto A. E. Bertelli, MD, PhD,** researcher, department of human anatomy, University of Milan.

Two compounds in white wine—*tyrosol* and *caffeic acid*—as well as extra-virgin olive oil help regulate the release of *cytokines*, chemical messengers in the body's immune system. Cytokines trigger the inflammation associated with rheumatoid arthritis.

SELF-DEFENSE: Ask your doctor about drinking white wine—and eating an olive oil–rich diet—to help prevent rheumatoid arthritis.

■

EAT VEGETARIAN TO RELIEVE ARTHRITIS

Source: **John McDougall, MD,** founder and medical director of the McDougall Program, a diet and exercise program in Santa Rosa, CA, *www.drmcdougall.com.*

A strict vegetarian diet helps to alleviate bothersome arthritis symptoms.

NEW FINDING: Rheumatoid arthritis patients who ate a diet containing no animal products or added fats or oils for four weeks experienced a significant reduction in symptoms, including pain and joint tenderness. The diet, which included corn, beans, fruits and vegetables, reduced levels of antibodies in the blood that attack joint tissues.

■

SPICY ARTHRITIS TREATMENT

Source: **Dharma Singh Khalsa, MD,** president and medical director of the Alzheimer's Prevention Foundation in Tucson, AZ, and author of *The Pain Cure* (Warner Books). He is board-certified in anesthesiology, pain management and antiaging medicine.

If you have arthritis, season your food with turmeric. Its primary constituent, *curcumin,* has been shown to be as effective at relieving pain as *cortisone* or *ibuprofen*—without any risk for side effects. A pinch or two a day is all you need.

■

CAYENNE: A PEPPER PAIN BLOCKER

Source: Uncommon Cures for Everyday Ailments, from the editors of *Bottom Line/ Health,* by Curt Pesmen (Bottom Line Books).

Among its many uses, cayenne is touted by numerous herbalists for its impressive efficacy against many kinds of pain, especially chronic pain, which is why it is well suited as a remedy for arthritis pain. Cayenne contains a compound called *capsaicin,* which, among other things, blocks pain impulses from traveling to the brain. As a bonus, the pepper is said to boost the production of endorphins, the natural painkillers produced by the body after exercise.

■

HELP FOR KNEE PAIN

Source: **Jane Servi, MD,** a sports medicine specialist in private practice in Fort Collins, CO.

Knee pain associated with arthritis can be eased with injections of *hylan GF 20* (Synvisc).

The drug curbs pain by increasing the viscosity of synovial fluid, which cushions the knee joint.

TREATMENT: Three injections, spaced one week apart.

Knee-pain sufferers who got these injections reported less pain while walking. Some needed less pain medication. Others were able to resume participation in the sports that they had abandoned.

A similar product, *hyaluronate* (Hyalgan), is given in a series of five injections spaced one week apart. In an unrelated study, this medication relieved knee pain for six months for most of the participants.

■

TOPICAL CREAM RELIEVES KNEE PAIN WITHIN FOUR WEEKS

Source: **Marc Cohen, MD, PhD,** president, Australasian Integrative Medicine Association, Melbourne, and professor and head, department of complementary medicine, RMIT University, Bundoora, both in Australia.

In a new study, osteoarthritis patients who applied a cream containing the nutritional supplements *glucosamine* and *chondroitin* experienced twice as much pain relief as those who used a placebo cream. Glucosamine and chondroitin *pills* have been shown to ease osteoarthritis knee pain, but researchers believe the cream may be more effective and faster acting, since it is absorbed directly into the knee joint. The cream is also free of common side effects, such as gastrointestinal discomfort, caused by oral anti-inflammatory medications that are typically used to treat osteoarthritis. Over-the-counter glucosamine and chondroitin creams can be purchased in pharmacies.

■

8 

TODAY'S MOST INCREDIBLE FREE WEB SITES

SOME WEB SITES ARE MORE FUN THAN OTHERS

Source: **Jim Glass, Esq.,** contributing writer to *Bottom Line/Tomorrow* who has written about information technology for many major consulting firms.

Here are nearly two dozen entertaining and useful Web sites—all available 24 hours a day, seven days a week...

• ***Listen to radio from around the world.*** Radio-Locator is a comprehensive radio station search engine, providing audio streams from 2,500 stations in the US and around the world. *www.radio-locator.com.*

• ***Play bridge.*** The playBridge Hand Generator creates bridge hands to play. There is a lot of other bridge information as well. *www.playbridge.com.*

• ***Plan a back-roads tour.*** Road tours across 35,000 miles of classic highways nationwide are described at Road Trip USA. Includes unique places to visit and roadside attractions to be found only off the interstate. *www.roadtripusa.com.*

• ***Trace your family tree.*** At Genealogy.com, you can tap into a huge genealogical database, take free genealogy classes and talk via message boards to other people with the same interests. You can also view celebrity family trees. *www.genealogy.com.*

• ***Find a drive-in theater.*** All drive-ins in the US are listed at The Drive-In Theater Web site. There is also a history of the drive-in and film clips of classic movie and concession advertisements. *www.driveintheater.com.*

• ***Be amused by the news.*** Get skewed news from *The Onion,* the top satirical "newspaper" on the Internet. *www.theonion.com.*

• ***Learn about the movies.*** The Internet Movie Database tells all about nearly every movie ever made in the US, plus their casts and crews. It also tells if a movie you want to see is playing on TV during that week. *www.imdb.com.*

• ***Get a translation.*** Automated translation services can be found through Babelfish. *www.babelfish.org.*

• ***Play chess.*** The Internet Chess Club has 30,000 members from around the world. At any given time, thousands—including several grand masters and international masters—are usually logged in. Play at any level in games of any speed...and make friends around the world. *www.chessclub.com.*

• ***Read celebrity biographies.*** More than 25,000 are on the *Biography* Web site at *www.biography.com.*

• ***Get the weather for anywhere.*** To learn the current weather and forecast for anywhere in the world, visit The Weather Channel at *www.weather.com.*

• ***Watch classic television.*** Thousands of videos of classic TV can be seen on demand at the LikeTelevision Web site. Shows such as *Alfred Hitchcock Presents,* celebrities such as Humphrey Bogart and Marilyn Monroe, classic commercials, cartoons and more. *www.liketelevision.com.*

• ***Improve your golf.*** The Golf101.com Web site has lessons on all parts of the game, plus golf news, a golf store and golf humor. *www.golf101.com.*

• ***Find the best price for gasoline and heating oil.*** Enter your zip code to find the best prices near you. Covers all 50 states and Canada and gives other useful fuel-buying information, too. Visit *www.gaspricewatch.com.*

• ***Listen to the Marx Brothers.*** A collection of classic humor of Groucho and the rest, including audio clips. *www.whyaduck.com.*

• ***Find anything.*** Craigslist is an Internet bulletin board and classifieds market where users can buy/sell/trade/find practically anything—from jokes to used cars...job listings to recipes. Go to *www.craigslist.org.*

• ***Read the classics or find a reference.*** Named the "Best Literary Resource" on the Web for 2002, Bartleby.com provides a large library of classic literature, plus reference works and nonfiction. From the ancient Greeks to the modern American essayists, with quotation compilations and much more. *www.bartleby.com.*

• ***Get free stuff.*** The Web's home for freebies is FreeStuffCentral.com. A huge array of offers and links to offers—from coupons to movie DVDs to free books to homes in foreclosure available with no money down. *www.freestuffcentral.com.*

• ***Listen to old-time radio.*** Fans of radio's Golden Age can listen to old programs and commercials at *www.old-time.com.*

• ***Check the time anywhere.*** Find out what the time is anywhere in the world. Other measuring unit converters as well as maps from the National Geographic Society are also available. *www.timezoneconverter.com.*

• ***Find eateries others overlook.*** Ordinary people reveal the best bargains, as well as the most unusual and most overlooked eateries they have discovered. Separate message boards cover each region of the US. *www.chowhound.com.*

• ***Find a music festival near you.*** Details on more than 2,500 festivals in the US are at Festival Finder. Search them by type of music, location, date or performer to find those you want to attend. *www.festivalfinder.com.*

• ***Get help with grandchildren.*** The Grandparents Resource Center offers assistance of all kinds for grandparenting—but especially for grandparents who are raising grandchildren by themselves. *http://grc4usa.org.*

■

VERY USEFUL WEB SITES

For a variety of helpful Web sites on a myriad of topics, check out the following list...

HEALTH...

• ***Alternative Medicine magazine,*** *www.alternativemedicine.com.* Features about all the latest health care issues and news on alternative treatments.

• ***Herb Research Foundation,*** *www.herbs.org.* Information about medicinal plants and how you can get the most benefit from them.

• ***Clinical trials,*** *http://clinicaltrials.gov.* The US National Institutes of Health's site, offering current information about clinical research studies.

• ***Eldercare Locator,*** *www.eldercare.gov.* The on-line Eldercare Locator, a service of the US Administration on Aging, helps seniors and their caregivers find local services.

• ***Healthfinder,*** *www.healthfinder.gov.* At this Web site of the US Department of Health and Human Services, you'll find information on diseases...insurance...health organizations...hospitals...and many other topics.

• ***Arthritis,*** *www.arthritis.org.* Loaded with information and support for people who suffer from arthritis.

• ***Eating disorders,*** *www.nationaleatingdisorders.org.* Help for all eating disorders, including anorexia nervosa, bulimia nervosa and binge eating.

• ***Panic attacks,*** *www.adaa.org.* The Anxiety Disorders Association of America can help you find a cognitive-behavioral therapist.

• ***Eat right,*** *www.eatright.org.* The American Dietetic Association offers comprehensive nutrition information on everything from diets to calorie measurements.

• ***Vegetarian Resource Group,*** *www.vrg.org.* Offers practical hints for vegetarian meal planning and articles relevant to vegetarian nutrition.

• ***Al-Anon,*** *www.al-anon.org.* A nonprofit organization helping families and friends of alcoholics recover from the effects of living with an alcoholic.

• ***Alcoholics Anonymous,*** *www.alcoholics-anonymous.org.* This self-supporting, nondenominational organization is available to anyone who wants to do something about his or her drinking problem.

• ***Domestic violence****, www.ndvh.org.* The National Domestic Violence Hotline provides crisis-intervention information on domestic violence as well as referrals to local service providers.

• ***Attention deficit/hyperactivity disorder****, www.chadd.org.* Information on ADD/HD for children and adults. Find support groups, answers to frequently asked questions and research information.

• ***National Women's Health Information Center****, www.4woman.org.* Directs you to a wide variety of women's health-related material.

FOR CONSUMERS...

• ***Appliance repair clinic****, www.repairclinic.com.* Troubleshooting and repair information for many types of appliances, from refrigerators to washing machines.

• ***Consumer action****, www.pueblo.gsa.gov.* Get the contact numbers of your city, county or state consumer-protection office. Go to "Consumer Help," then click on "Contact Information," then on "State Resources."

• ***Free shipping****, www.freeshipping.com.* Maintains a list of more than 1,000 on-line retailers offering good deals on shipping.

• ***Health insurance on-line****, www.ehealthinsurance.com.* This national on-line broker has access to thousands of health plans across the country and provides free comparison quotes.

• ***Compare insurance rates on-line****, www.insurance.com.* Provides articles and expert information on all types of insurance. You can also shop for insurance products and quickly compare rates and policy terms from a select group of the nation's leading carriers.

• ***Insurance quotes****, www.intelliquote.com.* Compare hundreds of insurance companies. Health, home, car and other insurance quotes are available.

• ***Consumer loans****, www.hsh.com.* Provides up-to-the-minute mortgage rates as well as credit, payment, refinancing and other calculators.

• ***Debtors Anonymous****, www.debtorsanonymous.org.* Help and other valuable information on compulsive spending.

• ***Locate an appraiser,*** *www.isa-appraisers.org.* Learn specific questions to ask before hiring a property appraiser, and what the appraisal report should and shouldn't include.

MONEY...

• ***Compute your net worth,*** *http://finance.yahoo.com.* Figure out how much you are worth by filling out a form provided on-line.

• ***Family financial planning,*** *www.msmoney.com.* Create a financial plan that works for your family, whether you are just starting out or planning to retire. Click on "Life Planning."

• ***Annuities,*** *www.annuitysite.com.* Answers all your questions about annuities—different types, benefits, how to choose, etc.

• ***Mutual fund watcher,*** *www.funddemocracy.com.* Articles on mutual fund practices, policies and rules that are harmful to shareholders. Keep up-to-date on the latest scams.

• ***IRA assistance,*** *www.irahelp.com.* How to protect your IRAs, 401(k)s and other retirement accounts from the IRS.

• ***Roth IRA basics,*** *www.rothira.com.* Learn all about Roth IRAs. The site includes articles, calculators, the latest news and more.

• ***Mutual Fund Investor's Center,*** *www.mfea.com.* Designed as a resource for investors who want to use mutual funds to achieve their financial goals, this site has a large collection of investing calculators, Web site links and fund listings, as well as planning, tracking and monitoring tools.

• ***Ric Edelman's advice,*** *www.ricedelman.com.* Ric Edelman, a well-known and respected financial adviser, gives his top 40 tips for investing. Click on "Financial Basics," then scroll down.

• ***Social Security on-line,*** *www.socialsecurity.gov.* Here you can apply for Social Security benefits, request a Medicare replacement card, get Medicare and Medicaid information, and more.

• ***Retirement locations,*** *www.retirenet.com.* Find the right retirement home—by size, price, location or any combination of factors.

• ***Estate planning links,*** *www.estateplanninglinks.com.* Contains hundreds of links to estate planning, elder law, tax and related Web sites.

• ***AARP The Magazine,*** *www.aarpmagazine.org.* Information to help you enjoy your health, wealth and leisure time. Read articles, play the games and take part in on-line discussions.

• ***Seniors' rights,*** *www.seniorlaw.com.* Covers elder law issues, Medicare, Medicaid, estate planning, trusts and the rights of the elderly and disabled.

HOME AND LEISURE...

• ***Garden know-how,*** *www.gardenguides.com.* Free electronic newsletters on a wide variety of gardening topics.

• ***China replacements,*** *www.replacements.com.* Here is a Web site where you can find more than 200,000 china patterns—some 100 years old and older—as well as hundreds of crystal and silver patterns that are offered for sale.

• ***Fix it yourself,*** *www.thisoldhouse.com/toh.* A comprehensive on-line resource for home-improvement articles covering kitchen, bath, yard and garden.

• ***Keeping clean,*** *www.queenofclean.com.* If you have a tough cleaning problem, you'll find the solution at The Queen of Clean. Covers carpet-stain removal, rust removal and a whole lot more.

• ***Spring cleaning,*** *www.cleaning.com/instructions.php4.* Tells you how to clean just about anything—aquariums, boat hulls, bathtubs, birdcages, computer equipment, leather furniture and more.

• ***Concerts, musicians and tickets,*** *www.pollstar.com.* See who's touring—when and where. The site also includes music news and ticket-sales information.

• ***Festival finder,*** *www.festivals.com/~finder.* Just click on the area of the world you'll be traveling to, and you'll get a list of festivals going on at that time.

• ***Half-price theater tickets.***

AUSTIN: *www.austix.com.*

CHICAGO: *www.hottix.org.*

LONDON: *http://home.clara.net/rap/half.*

NEW YORK: *http://timessquare.nyctourist.com/broadway_tkts.asp.*

SAN FRANCISCO (AND BAY AREA): *www.theatrebayarea.org.*

WASHINGTON, DC: *www.cultural-alliance.org/tickets.*

• ***Theme parks,*** *www.themeparkinsider.com.* Gives you news and reviews on many of America's theme parks, as well as information on discounts.

• ***Homework helpers,*** *www.homeworkspot.com.* A huge directory with encyclopedias, libraries, museum links, advice from experts and much more.

• ***Good manners,*** *www.emilypost.com.* Advice on everything from business etiquette to raising polite children.

■

HOW TO HAVE FUN GAMBLING ON-LINE

Source: **Bill Haywood,** Ohio-based author of *BeatWebCasinos.com: A Shrewd Player's Guide to Internet Gambling* (RGE).

Choosing an on-line casino can be a bit like selecting an auto mechanic. There are plenty of honest ones out there, but it can be tough to know which ones to trust.

The industry has attracted some shady operators who are quite willing to do whatever they can to take your money.

If you want to gamble on-line, here's how to do it right…

USE A REPUTABLE CASINO…

• ***Stick with the established Internet casinos.*** The Omni Casino (*www.omnicasino.com*), Casino-on-Net (*www.888.com*) and the MayanCasino Sportsbook (*http://sportsbook.mayancasino.com*) all have solid track records.

• ***Check the software.*** A casino is usually reputable if it uses software by Boss, CryptoLogic, Microgaming or World Gaming (originally Starnet).

FOR A LIST OF CASINOS BY SOFTWARE: Go to *www.winneronline.com.*

• ***Visit Internet chat rooms*** for the latest buzz on a casino in the on-line gambling community. Try *www.gamemasteronline.com* or *www.winneronline.com.*

• ***Make sure the casino has a toll-free number*** in case you have a problem. Dial the number before you gamble to confirm that it connects you to a person, not a recording.

• ***Try out the casino.*** Most on-line casinos let you play for free—some for as long as you like, others for a limited time. If the casino doesn't allow any free time, go elsewhere.

TRY AN ON-LINE PAYMENT COMPANY...

To place a bet on-line, you need to put up money on a credit card with the casino. If you win, you receive your winnings via the mail, a bank wire or a credit to your account with the casino or with an on-line payment company.

Many Internet gamblers are concerned about releasing credit card numbers to Internet casinos. Reputable, independent online payment organizations—such as FirePay (*www.firepay.com*) ...PayPal (*www.paypal.com*)...and NetTeller (*www.jackhenry.com/index.cfm*)—can act as intermediaries for you. At the casino's Web site, read the directions under "Setting up an Account" to see what forms of payment the casino will accept.

LOOK FOR NEW-ACCOUNT BONUSES...

Casinos often offer bonuses for new customers—as much as 20% of the amount the customer puts up. But you can't just set up an account and then cash out for a profit. Casinos have many rules governing these bonuses.

EXAMPLE: A casino might require any new players to make bets totaling the amount they originally deposited before their bonuses vest. You may be required to leave the money in for a specified time...or you may have to request the bonus by a deadline. Read the requirements carefully to make sure you know what you are getting into.

Be aware that casinos are not pleased when new account holders do just enough to qualify for the bonus and then try to cash out. One common complaint among Internet gamblers is that casinos—even the reputable ones—sometimes withhold bonuses even when all the requirements are met. This is not legal, but because most Internet companies are based overseas, it is not easy to enforce.

KNOW THE ODDS...

Whether you play on-line or in a land-based casino, some games stack the odds in the house's favor. All of the following odds are from *www.thewizardofodds.com.*

The house has a 5% advantage at roulette...as much as 15% at slots...and 29% at keno.

The odds are better with other games. The house has only a 2% to 3% advantage over the typical blackjack player. Advanced players can cut that to one-half of a percent.

With video poker, the house advantage can also be as low as one-half of a percent. To master the game, read *Video Poker–Optimum Play* by Dan Paymar (ConJelCo).

A craps player who sticks with *simple pass/don't pass* and *come/don't come* bets faces odds only slightly more than 1% in the house's favor.

Baccarat is probably the best choice for the novice gambler. It is easy to learn—and, like craps, the odds are only slightly more than 1% against the gambler.

Internet poker—different from video poker—is a recent development. You play against other players, not the house—and the casino takes a cut of the pot. Visit *www.poker.com* or *www.paradisepoker.com.*

COMPLAIN IF YOU RUN INTO TROUBLE...

If the casino is slow to pay, complain via phone and E-mail. Make it clear you are not going away quietly.

HELPFUL: *www.casinomeister.com* has a list of bad and good casinos.

WARNING...

On-line gamblers are more likely than land-based casino players to develop gambling problems. If you have ever lost more than you could afford at a land-based casino, avoid Internet casinos. If you think you need help, call the National Council on Problem Gambling's confidential 24-hour help line, 800-522-4700, or contact them on the Web at *www.ncpgambling.org.*

■

9 

AMAZING FREEBIES & SWEETHEART DEALS

FINDING MONEY THE EASY WAY

Source: **Mark Tofal,** a consumer advocate specializing in unclaimed property, Palm Coast, FL. His Web site is *www.unclaimedassets.com.*

State and federal agencies hold unclaimed assets for one in every four Americans. Unclaimed assets can be as big as an inheritance or as small as a utility deposit.

The older you are, the more likely you are to have unclaimed assets—especially if you have moved frequently or changed your name. If you do not communicate with a company—for example, by cashing a dividend check or notifying the company when you move—the asset is considered abandoned after one to five years. The number of years varies by asset type and state law.

Securities make up the largest category of unclaimed assets. Especially vulnerable are investors who have switched brokers or who hold their own shares—but never received statements, cashed dividend checks, claimed distributions (such as spin-off shares) or exchanged old certificates for new after a merger.

Most unclaimed assets are *not* on-line—so send an inquiry to the abandoned-property office in each state. Include your Social Security number, variations of your name—maiden name, nicknames—and previous addresses. You may even have assets in a state you never lived in.

You need to contact each federal agency directly to find out whether you have any money sitting with it. Be sure to include the IRS, Social Security Administration and Bureau of Public Debt.

■

FREE HOSPITAL CARE

If you don't have insurance coverage, even a very brief hospital stay can easily cost you tens of thousands of dollars and put you on the edge of bankruptcy. Fortunately, now there is something you can do. If you need hospital care but cannot afford it and have no insurance or if you have already been in the hospital and cannot afford to pay the bill, try calling the Hill-Burton Hotline. Through this program, hundreds of participating hospitals and other health facilities provide free or low-cost medical care to patients who are unable to pay.

You could qualify for this assistance even if your income is double the poverty-level income guidelines and even if a medical bill has already been turned over to a collection agency.

MORE INFORMATION: Hill-Burton Hotline. 800-638-0742, *www.hrsa.gov/osp/dfcr.*

■

FREE MEDICAL CARE

How would you like to have the finest medical care money can buy...and not spend one penny for it? That is exactly what thousands of people are doing every year thanks to the National Institutes of Health (NIH) Clinical Center. The NIH is funded by the federal government and is one of the nation's leading medical research centers.

At any one time there may be more than 1,000 programs under way where researchers are studying the newest procedures in the treatment of every imaginable disease, including all types of cancer, heart disease and diabetes, to mention a few.

If your condition is one that is being studied, you may qualify for free medical care at the NIH hospital in Bethesda, MD.

MORE INFORMATION: National Institutes of Health, Patient Recruitment, Warren Grant Magnuson Clinical Center, Bethesda, MD 20892-2655. 800-411-1222, *www.cc.nih.gov.*

■

FREE EYE CARE

The community service pages of your local newspaper occasionally will run announcements by organizations such as the Kiwanis or Lions Clubs. They offer free eyeglasses and eye exams to elderly people who otherwise could not afford them.

Also, check with your state's Office of the Aging. There is a wide variety of eye-care programs offered, and many include free eye exams and free eyeglasses.

To locate your state's office along with other resources, call 800-677-1116 or go to *www.eldercare.gov.*

■

CONTACT LENSES FOR FREE

If you wear contact lenses or are thinking of getting them, Johnson & Johnson would like you to try their Acuvue contacts for free. Go to *www.acuvue.com,* fill out the information requested and a free-trial pair certificate will be sent to you.

■

FREE OR ALMOST-FREE DENTAL CARE

Source: **Matthew Lesko,** Kensington, MD–based best-selling author of more than 100 books on how to get free services and products, including *Bottom Line's Big Fat Book of Free Money for Everyone* (Bottom Line Books), available at *www.bottomlinesecrets.com.*

There are over 50 dental schools in the US, all operating clinics that provide basic services at great savings. That includes checkups, cleaning, X-rays and fillings.

More advanced services such as fitting bridges, dentures and implants may also be available.

Student dentists do the work but are closely supervised by their professors.

BONUS: Care may even be free for conditions the professors are studying.

MORE INFORMATION: To locate a nearby dental school, log on to the American Dental Education Association's Web site at *www.adea.org.* Click on "Dental Schools & Allied Education Programs" and follow the links. Or call local universities and ask if they have dental schools.

Also, the dental society or association in each state has a list of dentists who volunteer their services to assist people who cannot afford proper dental care.

■

MORE FREE HEALTH CARE

Remember, if you live near a university that has a medical or veterinary school, typically, these schools will offer all kinds of medical or veterinary services for free or for a nominal fee. Call the schools in your area and ask which services are provided to the community.

■

HATS, BASEBALLS, T-SHIRTS AND MORE FOR FREE

Are you a big baseball fan? If you enjoy going to either pro or semipro baseball games, then you will want to check out the schedule of your favorite team and look for freebies. Oftentimes, teams will give out a certain quantity of free T-shirts, hats, baseballs and other sports items (many with the team's logo) just for being one of the first people at the game. Kids love to go to the games and this is a simple way to get something free with your favorite team's logo on it. Listen for any radio ads announcing these freebies, look for ads in the paper or call the home office of your favorite team.

■

MONEY TO FIX UP YOUR HOME

Is your home in bad need of repair, but you just can't afford the money to fix it up? Now there's help in the form of grants of up to $7,500 and loans as much as $20,000. The money comes from the USDA Rural Housing Service, which distributes loans and grants to improve housing and community facilities in the nation's rural areas.

To obtain a loan, home owners must be unable to get affordable credit elsewhere and have very low incomes. They must need to make repairs and improvements to make the dwelling more safe and sanitary. Grants are available to low-income home owners age 62 and older who cannot repay a Section 504 loan.

To apply for a loan or grant, contact the Rural Development office in your state.

MORE INFORMATION: Rural Housing Service National Office, US Department of Agriculture, Room 5014-S, Mail Stop 0701, 1400 Independence Ave. SW, Washington, DC 20250. 202-690-1533, *www.rurdev.usda.gov/rhs/sfh/brief_repairloan.htm.*

■

FREE CARS

Source: Reported in *The New York Times.*

Free cars are available from a company that uses them as traveling billboards. FreeCar Media of Los Angeles (*http://drivers.freecarmedia.com*) gives motorists two free years of use of a car that is wrapped in advertising slogans. Car users pay for insurance and fuel. Or, you can have the vehicle you own wrapped and get paid up to $400 a month.

OBJECTIVE: To have their cars seen in big cities.

Autowraps (*www.autowrapped.com*) pays people $200 to $400 a month to have ads placed on cars they already own.

■

BEST MAIL-ORDER AND ON-LINE RESOURCES

Source: **Gail Bradney,** consumer bargain expert, Bearsville, NY, and author of *Wholesale by Mail & Online* (Print Project).

There is no reason for shoppers today to wait for great sales on selected items at retail stores. You can buy almost anything you need at wholesale prices right now if you know where to go.

The companies on the following pages offer products and services starting at 30% below suggested retail prices. **ORDERING IN LARGE QUANTITIES CAN GET YOU AS MUCH AS 90% OFF...**

BED AND BATH TEXTILES...

- ***Bates Mill Store.*** Sturdy cotton bedspreads and blankets sold direct from this 1850s Maine mill—no middleman to up the prices. Bedspread seconds are marked down here an additional 40%. 800-552-2837, *www.batesbedspreads.com.*
- ***J. Schachter Corp.*** Down-filled luxury comforters and pillows. Buy a high-end comforter—$700 at top New York department stores—for at least 40% less. 718-384-2732.

CAMERAS/PHOTO SERVICES...

• ***Owl Photo Corp.*** Photofinishing and video transfer are cheaper than at any other mail-order photo lab. 580-772-3353, *www.owlphoto.net.*

• ***Porter's Camera Store.*** Photographic and darkroom equipment and supplies. The prices on cameras, video equipment and optics are slashed by about 60%. 800-553-2001, *www.porters.com.*

CHILDREN'S CLOTHING...

• ***Basic Brilliance.*** 100% cotton everyday wear at 30% to 70% off. 800-409-3835, *www.basicbrilliance.com.*

• ***Bunny Creek.*** Off-price "Internet only" children's clothing retailer that offers quality apparel for children at discounts of up to 70% off regular department store retail prices. 888-343-4825, *www.bunnycreek.com.*

FOOD AND BEVERAGES...

• ***Gibbsville Cheese Company.*** Wisconsin cheeses, specializing in cheddars, Colbys and Monterey Jacks. They sell sausages as well. Ships from October through May. 920-564-3242, *www.gibbsvillecheese.com.*

• ***Jaffe Bros. Natural Foods.*** Organic dried fruits—persimmons Fuyu, figs Black Mission, mango slices—and nut butters. 760-749-1133, *www.organicfruitsandnuts.com.*

HOME APPLIANCES...

• ***ABC Vacuum Cleaner Warehouse.*** Top brands and models up to 70% off. Free shipping on all vacuums within the continental USA with exceptions. 800-285-8145, *www.abcvacuumwarehouse.com.*

• ***EBA Wholesale.*** Save hundreds of dollars on appliances and pluggables—from air conditioners to refrigerators. Nationwide delivery. 888-728-3266, *www.shopeba.com.*

HEALTH AND BEAUTY PRODUCTS...

• ***AARP Pharmacy Services.*** You don't have to be a member of AARP to make use of this full-service drugstore. Generic medications at half the cost of the brand-name items. And an on-duty pharmacist is available to answer questions via phone six days a week. Honors most prescription insurance plans. 800-289-8849, *www.aarppharmacy.com.*

• ***Perfumania.*** Up to 75% off suggested retail prices on fragrances for both men and women. 866-557-2368, *www.perfumania.com.*

KITCHEN EQUIPMENT...

• ***Cook's Wares.*** Discounted gourmet ingredients, cookware and cookbooks. A Cuisinart Prep Plus 11 listed at $380 costs $199.99. 800-915-9788, *www.cookswares.com.*

LUGGAGE AND LEATHER GOODS...

• ***LuggageMan.com.*** First-quality travel and business bags and cases. A 29" Samsonite Oyster hardside listed for $200 costs $68.90. Buy five or more pieces of luggage and get an additional 10% off. 888-832-1201, *www.luggageman.com.*

JEWELRY...

• ***House of Onyx.*** Investment-quality, imported gemstones and jewelry at wholesale prices—50% to 60% less than you would find elsewhere. 800-844-3100, *www.houseofonyx.com.*

PET SUPPLIES...

• ***Omaha Vaccine Company.*** Prescription and nonprescription medications, grooming supplies and accessories for all animals—at up to 50% off retail prices. Many veterinarians buy here. 800-367-4444, *www.omahavaccine.com.*

• ***That Pet Place.*** Huge discount pet supplier for birds, fish, reptiles, dogs and cats. 888-842-8738, *www.thatpetplace.com.*

TOOLS AND HARDWARE...

• ***Harbor Freight Tools.*** Save up to 30% on tools, hardware, camping equipment, and lawn and garden machinery. 800-423-2567, *www.harborfreight.com.*

■

10 

HUSHED-UP SECRETS OF ULTIMATE SEX

HOW TO MAKE SEX EXCITING...AGAIN

Source: **Dagmar O'Connor, PhD,** a sex therapist in private practice in New York City, *www.dagmaroconnor.com.* She is author of the book/video set *How to Make Love to the Same Person for the Rest of Your Life—and Still Love It* (Dagmedia).

Passion is a powerful force in the beginning stages of most intimate relationships. Unfortunately, our hectic work schedules, child-care responsibilities—even Web surfing—can prevent couples from really nurturing their sexual relationship.

GOOD NEWS: You *can* restore the sexual excitement of your relationship. The key is to make time for sensual contact. Remember, arousal is just as important as orgasm.

In my 30 years as a therapist, I have found that the best way to become a passionate lover is to stop blaming your partner, and to start identifying—and communicating—your own needs in a constructive way. **HERE'S HOW...**

• ***Express your emotions and clear up any resentment.*** Sexual feelings are intimately linked to emotional expression. Many of us were raised to repress basic emotions—particularly anger or sadness. This can inhibit sexual response.

People who have sexual difficulties often grew up in families with parents who never raised their voices. Those who do not argue usually consider anger "unacceptable."

If you have difficulty expressing anger constructively, practice venting this emotion on your own. When driving alone in the car or showering, yell as loud as you can. After the initial embarrassment subsides, you may feel great. But you may feel sad later on. Anger often masks hurt or sadness.

• ***Tell your partner exactly what you want—and need.*** Many people are much better at expressing disappointment and anger than they are at communicating their desires.

Practice asserting your needs in all areas of your life. Being "nice" all the time prevents you from knowing what you are actually feeling.

SELF-DEFENSE: If you typically say "yes" to all requests, try saying "no" 10 times each week. Also practice making requests of others. Learn to be more "selfish."

• ***Become comfortable with your body.*** If you are feeling self-conscious about your physical appearance, you won't get very much pleasure out of sex.

HELPFUL: Relax in a bath a few times each week. Use the opportunity to look at and touch your body in a nonsexual way.

Stand nude in front of the mirror for a few minutes each day. Don't criticize your body. See it as an artist would. Appreciate what you have—don't dwell on your perceived imperfections.

WHEN PRIVACY PERMITS: Lounge around in the nude with your partner. If you feel like it, touch each other in nonsexual ways. Once you've established this sort of physical intimacy, taking the next step to sex becomes much easier.

• ***Put yourself in a sensual mood.*** Fantasy is one of the best ways to do this.

HELPFUL: For women who feel inhibited about being sexy, consider going into a store to try on provocative dresses or lingerie. You do not have to buy this stuff—just see yourself in a different way.

Share your sexual fantasies with your partner. It's not necessary to act out these fantasies—though you may choose to.

Your goal is to simply create your own sexy movies in your head.

• ***Concentrate on your sexual pleasure.*** Sex is not only an expression of love, it's also an opportunity to experience pleasure. Good lovemaking involves two partners "using" each other for their own pleasure.

Don't expect your partner to take care of everything. And don't be afraid to tell your partner exactly what pleases you and what you want from sex. You'll both benefit if each of you is willing to behave a bit selfishly.

• ***Develop a nonverbal language with your partner.*** Showing is inherently less critical than telling. Make a pact to communicate in a nonverbal way—by moving your partner's hand, for instance—if you find something unpleasant or pleasant during sex.

HELPFUL: Set aside 45 minutes to let your partner explore your body. Then reverse roles for 45 minutes.

• ***Touch each other often when not in bed*** to create a sense of closeness all the time.

• ***Take turns initiating sex.*** When to have sex is a big issue for most couples. One person might prefer it in the morning...the other at night.

If you started things last time, your partner should initiate the next sexual encounter.

IMPORTANT: For this to work, the noninitiating partner can't say "no."

• ***Schedule a weekly "date" with your partner.*** Set aside one night a week to be intimate. Do whatever you want—sensual touching, talking together or just reading the paper.

IF YOU HAVE CHILDREN: Hire a babysitter to take the kids out while the two of you stay at home. Take the phone off the hook and spend a few hours in bed.

To nurture your sex life at home, make your bedroom a place for rest and sensuality. Lock the bedroom door, banish the television from the room and avoid arguing or discussing problems while in bed—it should be a place for rest and pleasure.

■

10 FOODS THAT BOOST SEX DRIVE

Source: **Barnet Meltzer, MD,** founder of the Meltzer Wellness Institute and a physician in private practice in Del Mar, CA. He is the author of *Food Swings* (Marlowe and Company).

Foods rich in vitamin E, magnesium, niacin, potassium, zinc and the amino acid L-arginine all increase libido, boost sexual stamina and improve performance.

Top 10 "sexiest" foods...

1. *Celery.*
2. *Asparagus and artichokes.*
3. *Avocados.*
4. *Onions and tomatoes.*
5. *Almonds.*
6. *Pumpkin and sunflower seeds.*
7. *Romaine lettuce.*
8. *Whole-grain breads.*
9. *Fruits and nuts.*
10. *Chilies, herbs and spices,* such as mustard, fennel, saffron and vanilla.

■

HERBAL REMEDIES CAN HURT FERTILITY

Source: **Robert L. Barbieri, MD,** chief, department of obstetrics, gynecology and reproductive biology, Brigham and Women's Hospital, Harvard Medical School, Boston.

Recent lab studies suggest that certain herbal remedies do indeed make it harder to conceive. The herbal antidepressant *St. John's wort,* the immunity-booster *echinacea,* as well as the herb *ginkgo biloba,* seem to have adverse effects on eggs—and on sperm, too. *Black cohosh,* used to alleviate menstrual symptoms, can trigger uterine contractions and even miscarriage.

■

CURB BLOOD PRESSURE WITHOUT CURBING SEX

Source: **Carlos Ferrario, MD,** professor and director, Hypertension and Vascular Disease Center, Wake Forest University School of Medicine, Winston-Salem, NC.

One side effect of hypertension medication is sexual dysfunction. But among hypertensive men who took the blood pressure medication *losarton* (Cozaar) for 12 weeks, sexual satisfaction jumped from 7% to 58%. Those who reported having sex at least once a week increased from 40% to 62%.

IF YOU SUFFER SEXUAL SIDE EFFECTS FROM HYPERTENSION MEDICATION: Ask your doctor about switching to losarton.

■

WHO SCORES DURING PLAY-OFFS?

Source: The Medical Post, 1 Mt. Pleasant Rd., Toronto, Ontario.

Sales of drugs for erectile dysfunction fell by half in the United Kingdom during a World Cup soccer championship.

THEORY: Watching sports may be a natural stimulant...or men preoccupied with sports may lose interest in sex.

■

SNIFF BEFORE SEX

Source: Men's Health Magazine, 33 E. Minor St., Emmaus, PA 18098.

A new nasal spray promotes an erection in less than 15 minutes, half the time of *sildenafil* (Viagra). The spray contains *apomorphine,* a chemical that stimulates the brain receptors that trigger arousal. The spray could be on the market sometime in the next few years.

■

GET ROMANTIC

For hundreds of ideas on how to spice up your relationship, check out *www.getromantic.com*. Includes romance tips, a kissing guide, dating advice and much more.

■

LEARNING TO LOVE AGAIN

Source: **Mel Krantzler, PhD,** and **Pat Krantzler,** codirectors of the Creative Divorce, Love and Marriage Counseling Center in San Rafael, CA. Dr. Krantzler is author or coauthor of several books on relationships, including *Learning to Love Again* (HarperPerennial).

Each year, millions of older Americans seek new romantic connections after a divorce, widowhood or the breakup of a long-term relationship.

STUMBLING BLOCKS...

When contemplating a new relationship, many of us toss obstacles in our own paths. These mental blocks can prevent you from embarking on new romance. **COMMON OBSTACLES...**

• ***Fear of being rejected.*** "I'm too old, so nobody will want me" is an excuse we frequently hear.

WHAT WE TELL CLIENTS: Being older is now more of a plus than a minus. There are more people over age 50 today than at any other time in history. The world is full of people your age who are looking for a person like you.

• ***The saintly departed.*** Putting one's deceased spouse on a pedestal makes it easy to remember only the good and forget the bad. "No one else can measure up," you tell yourself.

WHAT WE TELL CLIENTS: You may be using this view as an excuse to prevent yourself from renewing your life and loving another person. Avoid the comparison trap—you can love someone else in a different way instead of the same way you loved your departed spouse.

• ***Survivor guilt.*** After a spouse's death, the survivor often feels guilty to be alive.

WHAT WE TELL CLIENTS: It's great that you had such a wonderful spouse. Don't you think he/she would want you to meet someone else now...and be happy?

- ***The burned divorcé.*** After a divorce, some people remember only hurt, anger and mistrust and forget the good times. The prospect of finding a new partner rekindles memories of pain, rejection and the loss of personal identity. "Why take the risk?" they ask. "Why let love ruin my life again?"

WHAT WE TELL CLIENTS: These arguments make one a victim, afraid to take a chance again.

- ***Fear of sex.*** Sex is a minefield today. People are terrified to start a new relationship. Many of our clients say they expect prospective sex partners to be tested for sexually transmitted diseases. One positive effect of this development, of course, is a reluctance to indulge in the instant sex that was the norm for a while. That hardly ever leads to a lasting relationship.

WHAT WE TELL CLIENTS: Feel free to tell prospective partners if you are not yet ready for sex after a painful divorce or breakup. Say, "I'd like to get to know you better by spending time with you first."

READINESS TIME...

Learning to love again typically involves four stages. Each stage may last weeks, months or years—or a lifetime. You may also reach a new stage only to slide back to a previous one.

- ***Remembered-pain stage.*** Any thought of a lasting love relationship feels like salt poured on an open wound. You send the signal, "Don't come close to me. I have been hurt too much." Self-pity, isolation and overindulgence in drugs or alcohol are very common.

On the other hand, this stage may bring on a wild rush to marry an improved version of the former spouse, in an attempt to be part of a couple again. You cannot entertain the idea that a relationship is based on being part of another person. Each of us is *already* a whole person.

- ***Questing/experimental stage.*** Recognition dawns that being a single person lets you respond to new challenges in new ways. Remembered pain diminishes in intensity. The realization then emerges that, like millions of other single people, you are free to try new relationships.

A person in this stage may join singles groups or have sexual affairs, but close commitment founded on mutual respect and caring remains inconceivable. You send out the message, "I'm sensitive, vulnerable and defiant. Don't ask for more than my body, because I have nothing more to give."

The diminishing appeal of purely sexual relationships signals readiness for the next stage.

• ***Selective-distancing stage.*** Eventually, the belief that one is half a person declines. The sense of being a competent single individual becomes dominant. Hassles with the ex-spouse have ended. Legal issues of inheritance and financial planning have been resolved.

The desire for new relationships begins to feel more like a promise of adventure and less like a guarantee of more pain. Rising self-esteem enables you to meet people through friends or hobbies...at parties, workshops, committees...in social organizations...in chance encounters at a museum or park.

The longer this stage lasts, the more intense the longing for a lasting love relationship. But the fear persists that a close commitment will end in disaster. You send the signal, "Come close, but go away. I don't want to be hurt again." Brief relationships are common.

Eventually, the balance of internal forces tips in favor of commitment. The courage to embrace an intimate relationship overpowers the fear of its possible failure.

• ***Creative-commitment stage.*** The final stage grows out of the recognition that what you feared was only fear itself. You send the signal, "Come closer at your own pace. I would like to know you better. I will be comfortable with whatever develops."

Trust in yourself leads to trust in others.

When intimacy grows and fits both parties, it is because it is founded on friendship, caring, warmth, vulnerability and love. That love includes mutual respect and trust, as well as sexual delight. One views the prospect of a monogamous commitment as a prospect to welcome rather than to avoid.

■